'I could marry you, I suppose.'

Bevin managed to cope with her astonishment, but not with the anger that quickly followed it. She could do without his offhanded and never-meant-to-be-taken-seriously proposals, thank you very much, and she wasted no time in telling him so.

'Don't do me any favours!' she snapped suddenly, the temper which had only surfaced since she had known him rising again as, her eyes flashing, she sprang up from the table.

Dear Reader

We are always keen at Mills & Boon to discover more about our readers' likes and dislikes. This month, we want to know what you think about our heroes! He is always in command and always a real catch, but do you like your hero to be just that little bit on the side of dangerous—ruthless even? Or do you like him to be gentle and caring, and unashamed to show it?

Do you like a gentleman or a rake? And what about foreign heroes? We'd love to know so put pen to paper and tell us.

The Editor

Jessica Steele lives in a friendly Worcestershire village with her super husband, Peter. They are owned by a gorgeous Staffordshire bull terrier called Daisy, who thinks she's human—they don't like to tell her otherwise. It was Peter who first prompted Jessica to try writing and, after the first rejection, encouraged her to keep on trying. Luckily, with Uruguay the exception, she has so far managed to research inside all the countries in which she has set her books. Her thanks go to Peter for his help and encouragement.

Recent titles by the same author:

HIS WOMAN
BAD NEIGHBOURS

DESTINED TO MEET

BY
JESSICA STEELE

MILLS & BOON LIMITED
ETON HOUSE   18-24 PARADISE ROAD
RICHMOND   SURREY   TW9 1SR

First published in Great Britain 1992
by Mills & Boon Limited

© Jessica Steele 1992

Australian copyright 1992
Philippine copyright 1992
This edition 1992

ISBN 0 263 77767 7

Set in Times Roman 10½ on 12 pt.
01-9210-52891 C

Made and printed in Great Britain

CHAPTER ONE

'WATCH your step! This is *my* house, remember!'

How could she ever forget! There had been the usual unpleasantness in her stepmother's tones, nor was the threat behind her words lost on Bevin, but for once she took little heed. She was feeling frozen, ached in every limb, and, although she was prepared to admit to having a heavy cold, she had a dreadful feeling that she was about to be visited with a giant-sized helping of flu.

'I'm going to bed,' she announced, and was on her way to rustle up a hot water bottle when the phone rang.

As she had taken to doing since she had moved in two weeks ago, her stepmother answered the phone. 'Who wants her?' Bevin heard her booming voice demand of the caller.

Bevin smothered a sigh and, while objecting strongly to Irene Pemberton's attitude, she went over to take the phone from her. 'Hello,' she said into the receiver, feeling much too weary to object to the fact that Irene was standing there ready to take in every word she said.

'Hello, Bevin, it's me—Oliver.' She went to reply but, before she could answer him, a bout of coughing took her. 'You've got a cold!' he exclaimed.

'A bit of one,' she underestimated when she had some breath back.

'I'll bring you something for it,' Oliver Taylor, the local pharmacist, immediately volunteered.

'Oh, there's no need,' she assured him quickly, 'I'm going to have an early night. I'll be better by morning.'

'If you're sure,' he replied, sounding concerned, and only when Bevin had convinced him that her cold was a mere trifle did he get round to the purpose of his call. 'Actually, you know I was thinking of having a week off—well, I've managed to get a locum in starting Saturday and—well, I wondered if you'd like to come away with me.'

'Oh, I don't think...'

'It'll be all above board,' he cut in hurriedly. 'My mother's been saying it's about time I paid her a visit, and I know she'd be delighted to meet you.'

Oh, heavens, Bevin thought unhappily. 'I'm sorry, Oliver, I just don't feel I want to go away right now,' she told him, caught her stepmother's sour-faced look and tuned back in to Oliver. 'Besides, I've started w...'

'I understand, of course I understand.' He was, as ever, quickly sympathetic. 'It was just that I thought, what with you losing your father so recently—not to mention all your other problems—that a change of scene might do you good.'

'That was very thoughtful of you,' she found the energy to respond, as a splitting headache joined her other symptoms.

'You're sure you wouldn't like to...?' Oliver pressed.

'Thank you just the same,' she replied.

'I'll ring you when I get back, then?'

'Have a nice time,' she bade him, and put down the phone to go in search of some aspirins.

'Frightened I might change the locks on the doors if you go away?' Irene followed her to taunt, clearly having realised that Oliver Taylor must have been asking her twenty-two-year-old stepdaughter to go away somewhere with him.

'You've had ample time to do that while I was out today,' Bevin answered, and, hating the atmosphere in her home that had been there ever since her step-mother had moved back in, she downed a couple of aspirin, filled a hot water bottle, and went up the stairs to her room.

Having thought she felt exhausted enough to sleep the clock round, however, Bevin discovered that her worries were such as to make sleep impossible. She thought of her father, but when weak tears started to well up she determinedly set her mind to think of happier times.

Though when was the last time she'd been truly happy? she wondered.

She'd been happy when her mother had been alive, she recalled. Her 'little miracle', her mother used to call her. Her father had married late in life, and her mother had been thirty-nine herself when she had married Edmond Pemberton and come to live in the sizeable village of Abbot's Cheney in Oxfordshire. A year later Bevin had been born, and her mother had been overjoyed. For a few moments Bevin basked in a happy memory of her mother, beautiful and with the same reddish-blonde hair she had passed down to her, a wide, loving smile on her lips, as she met her from school. Then Bevin was shaken by another bout of coughing, and the picture of her laughing-eyed mother abruptly vanished. Her next memory was of her father telling her that her mother, who had been at pains to teach her road safety, had been involved in a traffic accident herself—and killed.

Life had never been the same for Bevin after that. She had been eleven then, and had witnessed how her father, a man never very free with his smiles, had seemed not to have a smile for anyone over the next three years.

She had thought, though, that things were about to improve when, in her fourteenth year, her father had met and quickly married Irene Smith—but they had all been doomed to disappointment.

Irene, who had been married before, was pushing fifty and, it turned out, clearly knew what she wanted. Edmond Pemberton, retired accountant with more than adequate income from some sound investments, had thought Irene had wanted him—they had both very soon discovered a miscalculation. He, that Irene had more interest in getting her hands on his money than interest in him; she, that other than for general housekeeping expenses he had no intention of parting with any of his carefully built up nest-egg.

The rows about money were legion. Bevin was seized by another paroxysm of coughing, and struggled into a sitting position. Then, exhausted, her temperature soaring, she pushed the hot water bottle out of the bed and lay down again.

She closed her eyes, but, as her thoughts lingered on that last row between her father and Irene, sleep just wouldn't come. 'You're nothing but a penny-pinching old miser!' Irene's none-too-dulcet tones had floated upstairs to where Bevin, in her bedroom, was doing her homework. Bevin had ceased working on hearing her father's raised voice, but couldn't help hearing Irene's screeched, 'I'll get you! If it's the last thing I do, I'll get you!'

'Do your worst!' Edmond Pemberton had shouted back. And Irene had.

The very next day she had left the home which only a year previously she had moved into, to the neighbouring town of Dereham. The next Edmond Pemberton had heard was a letter from her lawyers in which she sought a substantial monthly allowance.

Her father had engaged solicitors of his own, but when their first account arrived, he had very soon come to the conclusion that he was being ripped off on all sides. Which was why he decided to do his own negotiating and, though it grieved him to part with the money, he had finally agreed a figure which he declared might be worth paying to keep the dreadful woman out of his home. And, since never again was he going to be so demented as to try marriage for a third time, he had no intention of paying lawyers' fees in filing for a divorce when, who knew, some judge with some half-baked ideas on the frailty of women might decide he could afford to pay the dreadful woman more than he was paying now.

Shortly after that, Edmond's health started to fail, and although Irene negotiated an increase in her allowance from time to time there was never any suggestion that she would come back to nurse him. She would have been horrified at the idea, while he— he would have been appalled.

There had been some talk, when Bevin had shown a natural aptitude for figures, of her training to be an accountant too. But when her father's health started to go from bad to worse, there was no question but that she should stay home and look after him. So she'd left school, and devoted herself to taking care of him.

'I'll make it up to you,' he told her one day when he was in one of his more mellow moods. 'This house, and all my investments—all I own—will be yours one day. I've seen to it.'

'Don't! Please don't talk like that,' Bevin had begged him, unable to bear the thought of him dying, of him one day no longer being there.

'Don't upset yourself, girl. It's got to be talked about,' he had replied.

'Yes, but—not today,' she'd pleaded, and he had dropped the subject and, as if aware how much it had upset her, or perhaps, on thinking about it, considered that he had said all that had needed to be said, had never referred to the matter again.

Some days were good, some were quite painful. Edmond Pemberton had a good doctor who called regularly and who prescribed specialised drugs which Bevin obtained from the chemist's shop in Abbot's Cheney. She never had any problems in changing the doctor's prescription until one week when the old chemist retired and a new man took over.

Which was how she came to meet Oliver Taylor. He was tall, thin and thirty, and was in fact the new and sole owner of the village chemist's. He was very willing and helpful too when, gazing down at the clear-complexioned, wide-brown-eyed twenty-year-old with long strawberry blonde hair who was waiting for him to go and make up the prescription, he questioned, 'This is for an Edmond Pemberton?'

'My father,' she explained, and had been going on to state that it was impossible for her father to come

for the dangerous drugs himself, when she realised
that the pharmacist seemed to know that.

'I'm afraid I haven't got all you need here, but I'm
expecting a delivery in about an hour.' And, as if
comprehending that she didn't like to leave her father
too frequently, 'I'll drop the remaining items in, if
you like.'

'It's not out of your way?' she queried gratefully.

'Of course not,' he smiled—and so Bevin made the
acquaintance of Oliver Taylor.

He became a good friend over the next two years
and would often pop in for an hour or so at the end
of his day. Apart from the doctor and the district
nurse, they had few other visitors, though, so her
father in particular welcomed Oliver's visits as a break
from routine.

Oliver had been there almost immediately when her
father had died three weeks ago, and Bevin had been
glad to have a friend she could turn to. He was there
at her father's funeral too, and, with so few people
there, she was again glad to see him.

An announcement of Edmond Pemberton's death
had been printed in the *Dereham Chronicle*. But of
Irene—an avid reader of that paper, so she must have
known of her husband's passing—there was no sign
at his funeral.

Bevin experienced another bout of coughing, but
her thoughts went on to how, at the time, she had
formed the view that, although Irene had been conspicuous by her absence, perhaps she was just being
honest. Neither she nor the man she married could
stand the sight of each other, so perhaps it would have
been hypocritical for her to have attended his funeral.

Less than twenty-four hours later, however, Bevin was shaken into having second thoughts about her stepmother's honesty. Shaken to indeed wonder if Irene Pemberton knew the meaning of the word honesty.

Painfully Bevin recalled how she had been upstairs in her father's room forcing herself to do some essential folding up of his clothes, when there was a ring at the doorbell.

She went down the stairs to answer it, but soon realised how out of place was the small surge of relief she felt to be released from her parcelling-up duty. For that relief was short-lived when she saw that her thin-lipped stepmother stood on the other side of the door.

'You're not any fatter, I see!' Irene began loudly as she glanced hostilely at Bevin's slender form. Then, just as though she still lived there, and with not a word of condolence, she brushed past Bevin into the hall.

Wordlessly, and since she didn't rate very highly her chances of being able to bundle the plump woman out again, Bevin followed and opened the door to the sitting-room. At the same time, money having been the last thing on her mind, she suddenly realised why Irene, with her track record, must have called.

'You know of course that the bank have frozen your father's account?' her stepmother charged before Bevin could decide whether she should invite the woman to take a seat.

'That's quite normal, I believe,' Bevin answered, in truth having no idea whether it was or it wasn't, but as her thoughts went on she quickly realised that if her father's account was frozen, then so too would be the standing monthly payment out of her father's bank account and into Irene's.

'Normal or not, I want my allowance!' Irene demanded. But while Bevin was unable to see any other reason why the woman should call in person, and was trying to decide if she was meant to write out a cheque for her on the spot pending her father's affairs being sorted out, Irene, though still on the issue of money, was stridently going up another avenue to further demand, 'And while I'm here, I'd like to know what provision your father left for me in his will!'

I wonder you waited so long, Bevin came close to saying, all at once realising that, when pushed, she could have some pretty sharp thoughts herself. But, since she wanted this awful woman out of the house and, if possible, without a slanging match, she replied quietly, 'I haven't seen my father's will myself yet,' and since her father had a down on the legal profession since his last dealings with a solicitor, she felt certain that no law firm held his will. 'The bank probably have it in their safe keeping,' she told Irene. 'I'll...'

'They haven't got it. They're holding nothing of his!' Irene cut her off.

'You've enquired?' Bevin questioned, amazed.

'Of course I've enquired. Nobody does me down, girl, and don't you forget it!' Irene retorted nastily.

For one of the few times in her life, Bevin felt really angry. It would not have taken much for her to have ordered the woman to leave. How on earth, after being married to her ladylike mother, her father could have believed—even briefly—that he was in love with this dreadful woman was beyond her. But from somewhere Bevin found sufficient control to realise that even if she got this woman to leave today, until she'd got what she came for she could well turn up on the doorstep tomorrow, and the next day, and the day after that.

So she mastered her anger, and offered with calm dignity, 'If you'd like to give me your phone number, I'll look for my father's will, and ring you this afternoon about anything that relates to you,' and discovered that, where money was concerned, Irene had no time to delay.

'I'm not waiting on your pleasure!' she stated bluntly. 'I'll help you look for it now! It'll be in his desk in his study, I shouldn't wonder!' she boomed, and, before Bevin could stop her, she was out of the room, and for a big woman, heading at speed for her estranged husband's study.

The search did not take long. Edmond Pemberton had been a neat and methodical man. Feeling sick to her stomach, Bevin stood by the study door, barely able to believe that this was happening, that this avaricious woman was ransacking her father's desk.

Then, 'Got it!' Irene exclaimed triumphantly, and in her haste to take the document out of its 'Last Will and Testament' envelope, she nearly tore it. But, as she started to read, her thin mouth began to turn further down at the corners, and Bevin started to suspect that her father had left very little to the woman he had married.

When Irene venomously spat out the words, 'The mean bastard! He hasn't left me a penny!' Bevin, with her father not buried a week, had had enough.

'You've seen what you've come for—now go,' she ordered.

'You needn't think it gives me any pleasure to come back here, Miss High and Mighty!' the dreadful woman retorted. 'I'm going, but I'll take this with me,' she bellowed, waving the will in the air.

What possible use the will was to the woman, Bevin had no idea. But, since it was not Irene's property to take, she offered, 'I'll make you a photocopy, if you like,' indicating the small but efficient copier that stood on a table at the side of the desk, 'but the original stays here.'

Bevin discovered she was shaking once the woman had gone. Nor could she stop thinking about the episode. She took up the will and felt the jerk of tears again to realise that, while leaving everything to her as he had once indicated, her father still hadn't relented sufficiently on his objection to solicitors' charges to have someone in a lawyer's office type out the document for him, for the will was written in his own hand.

Bevin swallowed back tears, and her thoughts went on to Irene, as she realised that Irene must have been considerably upset that she had inherited nothing.

Perhaps I should have written her a cheque, she thought in a weak moment, but then pulled herself together to realise that, until her father's estate was settled, she didn't have all that much money herself.

Bevin was back upstairs a couple of hours later when the phone rang. Wondering who it was, for she wasn't expecting a call—unless of course it was Oliver, who had taken to ringing up almost every day since her father had died, she went swiftly down the stairs to answer it. Then she wished she hadn't hurried, for it was her stepmother on the line.

Before Bevin could more than wonder what it was that Irene wanted now, however, Irene was losing no time in telling her gloatingly, 'I took that copy of the will to my solicitor,' and seemed, while she waited for that to sink in, to be almost purring.

Again Bevin thought Irene certainly wasn't one to drag her feet. 'Oh?' she enquired politely, having no idea at all why Irene should have taken the copy of the will anywhere.

'Oh, indeed,' Irene retorted, then brought out, with ultimate delight, 'So you'd better start packing your bags!'

Try as she might, and as yet not at all alarmed, Bevin could not work out what Irene was getting at. 'I'm afraid I'm not with you,' she replied—and very nearly collapsed at Irene's answer.

'Nor will you be!' Irene snapped, and went on, 'You didn't think for a minute that I'd stand for that old miser short-changing me, did you?' She paused, but only briefly, and then, as if she just couldn't hold it in any longer, she hurried on to drop her bombshell. 'According to my solicitor—and I've every confidence in him—that will isn't worth the paper it's written on to you. You, Miss Pemberton, get nothing. But I, as your father's wife, am entitled to everything.'

'You're . . . !' Bevin gasped, as she tried to think clearly.

'That's right, I am! And you,' Irene stated viciously, 'can clear out the master bedroom, and start packing your own things too—I'm moving in tomorrow!' With that, she ended her call.

Ten minutes later Bevin was still not believing what she had heard. Ten minutes after that, though, and tightening fingers of unease had her in their grip. So much so that another ten minutes later she was scanning the Yellow Pages, and a short while after that was phoning around to find a solicitor who could see her that afternoon.

Having found one, a Mr Ford who it seemed specialised in wills, she had no time to wait around for the hourly bus into Dereham. A taxi was a luxury which she was beginning to realise she might not be able to afford, but Bevin was aware by then that she would know no peace until she did know the rights and the wrongs of it. The idea of that awful woman moving in as she had threatened—no, *stated*—was appalling!

'Mr Ford will see you now,' smiled a receptionist when, having been early for her appointment, Bevin had sat for five minutes stewing with inner agitation.

'Thank you,' she murmured and, hoping that none of what she was feeling was showing in her face, she followed the receptionist to Mr Ford's office.

'Miss Pemberton,' he smiled, a slight man with a friendly look about him, as he came round from his desk to shake her hand. 'Take a seat,' he indicated, and, going back round to his desk. 'Now, how can I help you—a problem with a will, I think you said over the phone?'

'I've brought it with me,' Bevin told him and, taking it from her bag, she handed it to him. 'I...' she faltered, and suddenly felt most uncomfortable about talking over personal family matters with this stranger. But she strove to take charge of herself. Her father was dead now, and if she didn't stick up for herself, no one was going to do it for her. 'My father is now dead,' she made herself go on, 'and when I thought our home...well, I didn't actually think about it at

all until today,' she got sidetracked as she tried to explain. 'Anyhow,' she went on, 'I must have known
that the house would be mine without thinking about
it—my father once said as much. But today,' she
paused at the shocking memory of it, 'my father's
wife—from whom he was separated...'

'Legally separated?' Mr Ford, who had been
listening in silence, darted the question.

'No, I don't think so,' Bevin replied. But, as she
recalled her father's proclivity to parsimony, especially where the legal profession were concerned,
'No, I'm sure not,' she said, and as the lawyer silently
waited, she went on, 'Anyway, my father's estranged
wife—er—widow, took a copy of this will to her solicitor today, and then telephoned me to say that
everything, the house, and everything, is hers.'

'Let's have a look, shall we?' was Mr Ford's only
comment.

He took the will from its envelope, but as he began
to read, and his legal brain locked into gear, his expression became more and more serious. By the time
he reached the end he had begun to 'tut' and shake
his head, and Bevin began to fear the worst.

She was right to fear the worst, she soon discovered, for, a man who clearly had experience of
this sort of thing before, he told her, 'With due respect
to your father, Miss Pemberton, I do so very much
wish people wouldn't try to be so clever.'

'It's—er—he didn't do it properly?' she questioned
faintly.

'He did not,' Mr Ford replied, and there being no
way to soften the blow, 'It's all wrong. Totally wrong,'
he revealed.

'You mean that Irene...my stepmother was right?'

'I'm afraid so,' he answered. 'The will is full of ambiguities and incorrectly worded sentences.'

Oh, no! Bevin thought worriedly, but as Mr Ford went on to show her just where each ambiguity and each incorrectly worded sentence lay, she was gradually having to accept that her father, an accountant—a figures man, not a wordsmith—had made a complete nonsense of it. The way she had read it—probably because she knew her father had meant to leave her everything—she had read it quite plainly that he had left his estate to her. But now, as Mr Ford led her through a minefield of her father's attempt at legal 'wheretos, wherefores' and even a 'theretofore' on one part, so she began to see much more plainly that the will must be read another way—as if he intended Irene to inherit everything!

Mr Ford was a very thorough man at his job, however, and went over it all again with her so that, in the end, she could see that there was no doubt that in the places where her father *had* got it right, he had, by adding a word or two, made it completely *wrong*. And as Mr Ford finally showed her again where her father had left some sentences as meaning something totally different, Bevin just had to accept that if her father had not left a will at all, the outcome would most likely have been much better for her.

'I've come across this sort of thing so many, many times,' Mr Ford commented, making her feel not one whit better that apparently it was quite a common thing for would-be inheritors to be done out of their inheritance by a wrongly and amateurly drawn up will.

'But there must be something I can do!' she protested anxiously—and was grateful to Mr Ford when, on her behalf, he reached for the telephone and consulted a most senior legal mind, and read her father's will to him over the phone. She could tell, though, from the solicitor's remarks as he ended his call, that the man he had consulted was of the same opinion as himself.

'I'm sorry, Miss Pemberton,' he commiserated as he put the phone down, 'Sir Michael has just endorsed my own view.'

'And there's nothing I can do?' she questioned, and knew it was hopeless when he shook his head.

'I'm afraid not,' he told her solemnly. 'You could try contesting your stepmother's claim, of course. But I have to tell you that it's my belief you'd be wasting your money.'

Money, Bevin was beginning to realise, was a commodity she suddenly had less of than she had thought. If she had to move out of her home—and no amount of not wanting to face that staggering fact was going to alter that outcome—then what with rent for some other accommodation and day-to-day living expenses, she reckoned she'd be hard put to it to survive for longer than three months.

Thanking her lucky stars that her father's last birthday gift to her, since though still mobile he had been unable to go out and shop, had been in the shape of a cheque, 'There doesn't seem to be any point,' Bevin said, then thanked him, and stood up.

'What will you do?' he enquired sympathetically as, handing her back the will, he walked to the door with her.

Holding back a sad sigh she answered dully, 'Go home and pack, I expect.'

'Oh, you've no need to move out straight away!' Mr Ford exclaimed. 'Things legal don't happen overnight,' he confided, giving her an encouraging smile. 'It could be quite some time before your stepmother has a legal right to demand that you leave. Quite some time,' he added, 'before your father's estate is settled.'

Out of all she had heard in the last half-hour, that piece of news was the brightest. Countless were times she had heard of estates taking as long as a year, longer in some cases, to be settled. It was with a heavy heart, though, that she shook hands again with Mr Ford and caught a bus back to Abbot's Cheney and let herself back into her home.

It wasn't fair, it just wasn't fair, she thought as she went and put the will that did her out of her rights back in her father's desk. From her father's study she moved around the house lovingly touching objects she had grown up with, but was unable to get away from the knowledge that tomorrow her father's widow would be moving in.

She remembered thinking how Irene had perhaps been just being honest by not attending Edmond Pemberton's funeral, but she knew then that it wasn't honesty that had kept her away. The woman just didn't care. Indeed, as Bevin thought of how, when it was plain to all but those in the legal profession that her father had not intended his wife to have his home, what honesty was there in the woman that she was claiming it anyway?

Bevin had not been home long when a ringing at the doorbell brought her from her unhappy thoughts. She checked her watch as she went to the door, saw it was some time after six, and guessed that her caller might be Oliver Taylor on his way home from his pharmacy and store.

It was Oliver, and although she hadn't thought she'd be telling anyone of the tremendous shock she had received that day, she had reckoned without her appearance giving her away.

'You look dreadful—as white as a sheet!' he exclaimed, as she invited him in and he went with her down the hall and into the kitchen. 'Isn't it getting any better?' he sympathised as Bevin, deciding to join him in a cup of tea, set the kettle to boil.

'It's not that,' she told him, realising that his sympathy was on account of her having to come to terms with the fact of losing her father. 'I've—um—had a visit from my father's widow. She's . . .' She made a pot of tea and sat down at the kitchen table with him to drink it, and bit by bit, she revealed the happenings of that day.

'But that's iniquitous!' he exclaimed, aware from village gossip of the existence of a second Mrs Pemberton, but as astounded as Bevin had been to learn that she had every intention of taking Bevin's inheritance.

'Iniquitous or not, it seems she's moving in tomorrow, and has every right to do so.'

For some more minutes they talked over the subject, then, 'What are you going to do?' Oliver asked, seeming, Bevin thought, to be oddly tense all of a sudden.

She shrugged the notion away—she was imagining things. 'Ultimately, though not tomorrow, as Irene wishes, move out. Then get myself a job, I expect,' she told him—and got the shock of her life when suddenly one of his hands came across the table, and he took hold of her right hand that had been idly playing with the spoon in her saucer.

Startled, she looked up, and got another shock. Nor was it her imagination that Oliver seemed tense, for to her astonishment he suggested, 'You could—could marry me.'

'Marry you!' she gasped, and stared at him in total surprise—there had never been anything remotely romantic between them so far as she was aware. 'I . . .' she managed but, quite honestly, was at a loss to know what to say.

'I hadn't meant to say anything so soon,' Oliver rushed in to state. 'What with you having your hands full looking after your father, I'd meant to wait. But you must know how I feel about you, and . . .'

'I—er . . .' Bevin felt she really should cut him off before he went any further—was this her day for surprises! 'I—um—don't think I'm ready for marriage yet,' she told him quickly.

'I've spoken too soon—too soon after your father's death,' Oliver apologised, and Bevin began to feel terrible, and again felt stuck for words. Perhaps she'd been incredibly naïve, but she just hadn't seen Oliver's visits as stemming from some feeling for her—but more as a kindness of someone calling to chat an hour or so away with her father.

'I—er—think I'll get a job,' she told him lamely, and to her relief he let go of her hand, and appeared to realise that he *had* spoken too soon.

As far as Bevin was concerned, much too soon. In fact, kind though he was, extremely nice person that he was, she just didn't and never had seen him in that sort of light, and she would far rather he hadn't said anything about marriage at all. It changed things, made her wary, and less at ease with him.

Bevin started coughing again now, realised that she must have dozed off, and sat up for several minutes before, her coughing bout subsiding, she lay down again.

Irene had moved in the next day, she recalled, and life had become little short of hell. Irene had been at pains at once to show who was mistress of the house—and there was little that Bevin could do but take it.

Her stepmother went through every cupboard and drawer in the house, took personal charge of the original of the will and, as well as issuing her orders as though to suggest that since she was living under her roof Bevin could act as unpaid housekeeper, she seemed to take a delight in making life generally unpleasant for her stepdaughter.

To a degree she succeeded, too, for where once Bevin had always found her home at Abbot's Cheney a most lovely place to live, it was now all spoilt.

I'll have to move out, she realised. The whole atmosphere of the house had changed. Somehow, though, Bevin couldn't bring herself to leave. Somehow, it was as if she would be letting her father down, as if she was moving out against his wishes.

She wouldn't be letting him down by getting herself a job, though, she decided, and if she did manage to get herself a nine-to-five job, then at least in between those hours she would be away from Irene's acid tongue.

Oliver called one day and Bevin introduced him to Irene, but when Irene determinedly hogged the conversation he did not stay long. 'How are things going?' he enquired when Bevin went with him to the door to see him out.

'Fine,' she lied, but since lying was alien to her, she quickly changed the subject, and added, 'I've applied for a job.'

'Doing what?' he enquired.

'Well, I'm not qualified to do very much except keep house,' she told him, and revealed, 'There's a market research job going. The firm's in Illington,' she went on, mentioning a town on the opposite side of Abbot's Cheney to Dereham, 'but if I get it, the work will be in Dereham.'

'Yes, but what sort of work will it be?' Oliver pressed.

'Standing outside supermarkets and asking passers-by a list of questions, I think,' she replied.

'Do you *want* to do that sort of work?' he asked, looking worried.

Bevin wished she knew. She was unqualified for anything, and without experience of the outside workplace, but she felt ready just then to grab at anything that, as well as enabling her to get away from Irene for a while, gave her the chance to earn some money.

'I'm not sure,' she answered, and because he looked so worried she smiled and told him, 'But since, if I do get it, it's only a temporary job, it won't be ...'

'I could offer you a permanent job,' he cut in impulsively, then went on before Bevin could feel more than briefly embarrassed that he might be asking her to marry him again. 'You could come and work for me in the shop. I'd like that,' he added for good measure.

Like him though she did, Bevin didn't think too much of the idea. For one thing, Oliver already had two assistants and she was sure he did not really need a third. For another, she needed some hours away from Irene daily. A job just round the corner in his store was much too close to home.

'Shall I see how my application goes first?' she suggested.

To brighten up her dark horizon she was called for interview a few days later, but had to wait another few days before she had a phone call to say she had been successful.

She was feeling very pleased with her success, and had made another trip into Illington last Friday, where she was given a short period of training which included how to fill in the questionnaires. Unfortunately the questionnaires she would use were not to hand from the printers yet, but would be posted on to her. So, armed with a folder and clipboard combined, and with instructions to start work the following Thursday for ten days, she returned to Abbot's Cheney.

By Monday, however, she started to go down with a heavy cold, but, since everybody caught a cold from time to time and just got on with it, she cleaned and polished around, and prepared a meal for that evening, while Irene watched television.

On Tuesday and on Wednesday Bevin anxiously looked for the post for the questionnaire forms which she could not work without, but they did not arrive. Contrarily, when on Thursday she felt so groggy with her cold she was half hoping that the forms would not come so she could spend the blustery February day indoors, they did arrive.

Slitting the envelope to check its contents, she left them in the envelope to keep them together and placed them in her folder, then went to get dressed in something warm.

'What time will you be in tonight?' Irene demanded as Bevin went to leave the house to catch the bus into Dereham.

'I've no idea,' Bevin answered, received a sour look for her trouble and went to do her first day of paid employment, to come home feeling frozen, ill and unhappy and to know that tomorrow she was in for more of the same.

She was therefore in no mood for any of Irene's acid when, as she stepped through the front door, Irene came out to meet her and demand, 'What's for dinner tonight?'

'You tell me!' Bevin had rebelled. 'I'm not cooking tonight!' and had thereby earned herself Irene's,

'Watch your step! This is *my* house, remember!'

Bevin shuddered in her bed, was shaken by another bout of coughing, and finally settled down to a few hours' sleep with the grateful thought that tomorrow, thank goodness, she wasn't scheduled to start until much later.

Sheer stubbornness not to give way to what she was still insisting was no more than a heavy cold aided her in struggling out of bed on Friday. She owned that she felt like death, as she made a pot of tea and downed another couple of aspirin. At the back of her mind she knew it would be sensible to ring her temporary employers and tell them she was under the weather, but, against that, there weren't too many jobs around that she could do, and she didn't want to get a reputation for being unreliable. Besides, once her name was on the firm's books, they might—were she reliable—have more work for her in the near future.

'You might have brought me a cup of tea up!' Irene complained, her ample dressing-gown-clad form sailing disagreeably into the kitchen where Bevin had been sitting with her eyes closed.

Jerked unceremoniously out of her few minutes of peace and quiet, her cold of no help either, Bevin came close to the end of her endurance. 'Sit down and I'll sing to you!' she retaliated—and was soundly rounded on for her trouble.

'That's *it*, you insolent bitch! My stars, is that it!' shrieked Irene, her screeching voice splitting Bevin's pain-filled head asunder. 'I'm getting on to my solicitor today, make no mistake about that! The minute this house is made over to me, out you go! Sooner, if I have my way!'

Bevin did not know if she would be able to stick it out for even that long in her old home, so, taking her cup and saucer with her, with Irene hurling abuse after her, she went upstairs and stayed in her room until it was time for her to catch the bus into Dereham. Oh, how she wished her father had had his will drawn up in the proper fashion!

The scene with Irene, her shrieking abuse, and thoughts of her father, were constantly on Bevin's mind as she stood in Dereham's High Street trying to pretend that her head wasn't aching or that she wasn't feeling dead on her feet and would have given anything for the comfort of a warm bed.

But she wasn't in a warm bed, and the wind was more biting than it had been yesterday, and she felt so cold she was going dizzy from it. Desperately she strove to pull herself together. Her task that day was to question people who had been categorised into various sections. It hadn't taken her long to complete her women shoppers aged twenty-five to thirty-five and with two children. Others were relatively simple too. The four retired semi-professional couples had taken longer than she'd thought to find, but, with that group now completed, all she needed now were a couple of professional men thirty-nine or under. Now where on a late Friday afternoon was she likely to spot them?

Her head began to swim again, causing her to grip tightly on to her clipboard and folder as she fought for control. But, as she conquered the sensation and was in charge of herself again, she remembered that there was an upmarket gents' tailors down at the other end of the High Street. She turned round, and was just about to make her weary way down to the other end of the High Street, when suddenly she halted. A long sleek and elegant car had just slid into a vacant parking spot, and a tall fairish-haired man of athletic build, aged around mid-thirties, she would guess, was just stepping from it. There was something about the man too that not only shouted professional, but aristocratic also.

But as he turned to lock his car, so as Bevin moved forward she knew she would have her work cut out to catch up with him if he took off with his long-legged stride. She put on a spurt then, but as he crossed from the driver's door in front of his car and on to the pavement, he seemed to notice that he had parked his car outside a travel agents and, miraculously, he paused, and seemed to halt indecisively.

Somehow she felt that that was odd. Somehow, and she couldn't have said why, she had a feeling that he was a man who would always know where he was going. But she had no time to waste in thinking inconsequential thoughts, and so, by putting on a spurt, she managed to reach him just as he was about to move on again.

'Excuse me!' She attracted his attention, her voice hoarse, her breathing laboured. To her gratitude, he stayed and looked down at her. But as she stared up at him Bevin thought fleetingly that he seemed a bit fed up with his lot. But she had done herself no favours by hurrying, and as waves of mist attacked, she was having the hardest job to remember what she should say next. 'I wonder if you'd mind...' was as far as she got before a wave of dizziness overwhelmed her that this time was beyond her control, and she felt herself falling.

Fortunately, she fell forward—against him. He was lean, hard and solid. 'Not at all,' she heard his cultured tones above the top of her head, 'but...' he was taking her clipboard from her '...I'd say you need somewhere to sit down first.' And so saying, clearly a man of action, and a seat in his car being the nearest one around, he quickly unlocked the passenger's door, and holding on to her with one hand, he as quickly opened the door, and with Bevin hardly conscious, he moved her unprotesting form inside.

Gradually the waves of dizziness began to disperse, and Bevin began to feel better for having something solid beneath her. She was still feeling not quite ready to go about her business, however, but though still feeling a degree or two woolly-headed, she realised, without alarm, that while she had not so long ago been standing out there on the pavement, she was now incarcerated with a mid-thirties professional-looking stranger in his car, and that he was in the driver's

seat, not driving, but was half turned and was looking
at her as if to ascertain how she was feeling now.

'I'm—sorry,' she croaked, her voice anyone's but
her own as she fought for the energy she must find
to go out into the biting wind again.

'You're ill,' he stated. 'If you'll tell me where you
live, I'll give you a lift home.'

Home, she thought bleakly, and found that, quite
ridiculously, she was telling him, 'It's all spoiled now!'

'What's spoiled?' he asked, and was a man of sharp
intelligence, she realised as, 'Home?' he questioned.

But she was feeling woozy again. 'I'm sorry,' she
mumbled, and lightheadedly forgot what his question
was when, as if to relieve him of all obligation, she
added, 'I don't think I would have fainted,' and gath-
ering up every scrap of strength she could find, she
reached over to the car door handle—only to have her
hand fall back when fresh waves of dizziness attacked, and, the only apology she could think to make
as she fought to stay conscious was another, 'I'm
sorry,' followed by, 'I don't think I've eaten today.'

'Can't you remember?' the man asked sharply, but
all at once Bevin was feeling totally exhausted and
used up, and couldn't have answered had her life de-
pended upon it.

She was vaguely aware of a pause, of a silence, but
it was beautifully warm in the car, and she wanted to
sleep and sleep. She closed her eyes for a moment,
but opened them again when the man leaned over her.
She relaxed, and closed her eyes again as she saw that,
clearly another decision made, he was just reaching
for the seat-belt to strap her in.

She still had her eyes closed when she heard the car
engine fire into life. She tiredly tried to open them

again when, watching what he was doing and not her, the stranger steered the car out of its parking spot. But it was too much of an effort to keep her eyes open, and, as the car picked up speed as the stranger drove off with her down the High Street, her eyes closed again. Oddly, she felt in no way threatened to be strapped in and carried off. Most peculiarly, she felt safe and secure. Indeed, safer and more secure than she had felt in a very long while!

CHAPTER TWO

BEVIN was sound asleep when the car stopped. Something disturbed her, though, and as a sudden waft of cold evening air caught her she started to cough, and opened her eyes.

The man, the stranger, the one who had been giving her a lift—though a lift where to, she couldn't for the moment remember—had vacated the driver's seat and had come round to her side of the car. Hazily she pulled herself together to realise that he had opened the passenger door and was once more leaning across her, this time to unfasten her seat-belt.

Swiftly she turned her head so that she shouldn't cough in his face. But, in case she already had, 'I'm—sorry,' she offered on a gasp of what breath she could spare.

'Can you manage to get out on your own?' he asked, going straight to the heart of the matter and ignoring her apology.

'Yes,' she answered, and was so busy concentrating on trying not to show that she would by far prefer not to move, while at the same time trying to control a bout of coughing that was insisting on not being controlled, that she gave no thought to what she did think she was doing. 'Thank you,' she said huskily when a pair of strong hands came and assisted her out anyway.

Then, as her breath fractured, and a fresh bout of coughing racked her, 'Come on,' he decided, 'let's get you inside.'

Bevin had little energy but to obey. But while she had not breath to speak, she had eyes to see, and she looked around to see where he was taking her. They were headed for the entrance to a very smart apartment block, she observed. The stranger kept a supporting hand on her arm and they were soon inside a well lit area over by some lifts. That was when some streak of caution suddenly, if belatedly, decided to give Bevin a nudge.

'Where are we?' she asked.

'My apartment,' he replied briefly, stabbing a long sensitive finger at the lift call button.

'Are we still in Dereham?' she wanted to know.

He turned his attention back to her, his expression cool, unemotional. 'The north side,' he confirmed— the smart side, she realised, and because she knew more of the shops in Dereham, the residential side was a part she was not too familiar with.

'Will your wife be home?' she asked, sorely needing to lie down somewhere warm and comfortable but her head overruling her unguarded instinct. Her experience of the male of the species was limited to her father, Oliver Taylor, and a mild dalliance with a youth at school when she'd been in the sixth form.

All at once, though, she found she was staring worriedly up into a pair of very nice, if all-seeing, all-comprehending grey-blue eyes. 'I'm not married,' he told her in suddenly clipped tones. 'Nor, if your ringless fingers are anything to go by, are you.' Bevin was still staring up at him, hazily noting that he must be astonishingly observant when he continued, 'You're

out on your feet,' and, his expression severe, 'It's plain
to anyone that you've used up any strength you had
in staying vertical to do your job. But since it's equally
plain you've no one to care for you or they'd never
have allowed you to leave your bed today—and since
it seems you've picked me—you can rest at my place
for a while, then, when you've got some strength back
and feel more able to cope, I'll drop you back to where
you live. Or,' he ended, 'if you prefer, I'll put you
into a taxi.' The lift arrived, the doors opened, and
Bevin was still staring at him from wide brown eyes
when suddenly he smiled—and she was transfixed.
Never had she seen such a charm-filled smile. 'Trust
me,' he bade her quietly and, as she stared fascinated
at his superb mouth that was now curving upwards,
charm had entered his voice as he enquired, 'Do you
seriously imagine that I'd want to risk catching your
germs?'

'If you put it like that,' she murmured huskily,
stepping into the lift, and, while feeling light-headed,
she at the same time realised that this heavy cold had
some most peculiar symptoms because, the strangest
thing of all, she was unexpectedly feeling most light-
hearted too!

He had been right about her using up her strength
to keep vertical while she did her job, she owned, as
the lift stopped at the third and top floor. For when
he took her along a corridor she was feeling muzzy-
headed and quite drained of energy again.

She was aware of his glance down at her as he unlocked the door to his apartment, but just then she
was more concerned with not passing out than with
returning his look. She was very glad of his suddenly
supporting arm about her, though, when he led her

into a thickly carpeted hall, and then into a similarly thickly carpeted sitting-room.

'Shall I take your coat?' he suggested.

'I'm a bit cold, actually,' she told him, and did look at him then, to see that he was taking on board the fact that, in his pleasantly centrally heated apartment, she was still feeling cold.

'Let's get you sitting down anyhow,' he said, and guided her to a couch that, as she sank down on to it, was pure and utter bliss and, to Bevin, like a feather bed. 'Have you seen a doctor?' the man enquired.

'It's not necessary,' she replied. 'It's only a heavy cold.'

'Looks like flu to me,' he commented.

'Are you a doctor?' she asked tiredly.

'No,' he answered, but his voice was not near, and she looked around in time to see him disappearing through another door.

I shouldn't be here, she thought, but had no strength to do anything about it, and started to feel warmer. She glanced about, and saw that the sitting-room was expensively if plainly furnished. Clearly a man's sitting-room, very neat and tidy, immaculately so, and with not a thing out of place.

The man came back, but only to check on her, she realised. 'Are you all right?' he asked.

She nodded. 'Do you look after yourself?' she heard her voice, husky with cold, question, and saw his charm again when he shook his head.

'You've caught me on a good day. I've got this excellent woman who comes and cleans up on a Friday. After that it gets progressively worse until the next Friday.'

Bevin didn't believe him, but didn't know whether she would have said so, because he disappeared again. She began to feel warmer still, and took off her scarf and undid her coat. Thank goodness she had finished coughing, though she mustn't get too thankful, for it could start off again at the least expected moment.

She looked longingly at the padded arm of the couch, and thought it would be the most wonderful thing in the world to rest her tired head there. Had she been in her own home, she might have done just that, she mused. But she wasn't in her own home— and anyway, there just wasn't any comfort in her own home any more.

She blinked back weak tears, and was suddenly terrified that, on top of landing herself on a complete stranger, she might well break down and have a sobbing session into the bargain.

Grief, she pulled herself round—this flu was taking the moral stuffing out of her! She closed her eyes and her head fell nearer and nearer to the padded arm of the couch.

'I've made you some soup!' The stranger's voice— although, oddly, he no longer seemed like a stranger— caused Bevin to jerk to with a start. 'You're done in, aren't you?' he sympathised, but suggested, lowering the tray he carried on to her knees, 'Get some of this down you, and you'll feel better, I'm sure.'

'Did you really make it?' she asked, her disbelief evident as she dipped her spoon into a bowl full of the most delicious mulligatawny soup.

'Not quite,' he confessed. 'But I did open the tin.'

Where Bevin found the energy from to laugh, she couldn't have said, but she did. There was just something about this man that she just couldn't fail to react to. She looked up and saw that his glance was on her smiling mouth, then his glance moved up to her eyes. Their glances locked—but he was in no hurry to look away.

'That's better,' he commented casually. 'You've got some colour in your face at last.'

'I'm feeling warmer now,' she replied, and finishing the last of her soup, 'That just has to be the tastiest meal I've enjoyed in ages,' she thanked him.

'I'll tell my chef,' he remarked, and took the tray from her and went to deposit it in the kitchen, to come back to suggest, 'If you want to feel the benefit of that coat when you go out, it might be an idea to take it off now.'

Now, Bevin realised, was the time when she should thank him most sincerely for all he had done for her, and to tell him she would now leave. But it was nice here, and it wasn't nice at home any longer. There was a pleasantness here in this man's home, and there was no pleasantness at all where she lived. So, even as she opened her mouth to tell him she would be on her way, 'Thank you,' she told him, and struggled out of her coat.

I shouldn't have done that, the well-brought-up side of her realised as the tall, firm-chinned, fair-headed man came back from putting her coat away in his cloakroom. She still felt warm, though that wasn't surprising since she still had on a pair of woollen trousers and a shirt and a sweater.

'What about *your* meal?' she asked and, as the thought came to her, in sudden fear that she had outstayed her welcome, 'I'm sorry,' she rushed to apologise, 'you've probably got an engagement this evening, a dinner date, and are just waiting for me to go.' She was struggling to get out of the clutching comfort of his gorgeous couch. 'I . . .' she rushed on, only to collapse in a fit of coughing.

'There you are, you see!' he exclaimed, and coming over to her, turned her until she was sitting with her back supported by the arm of the couch. And, in a lull from her coughing, 'Just relax and leave it to me to tell you when I want you to be gone. I'm quite capable of it,' he commented, and, for all his charm, she knew he was. Knew too, as if for a fact, that if the occasion demanded it he could be really tough.

She started coughing again, and he went away, to come back with a glass of water, and she took a sip. Then, when the irritation was for the moment eased, he moved a small table close to her and placed the remainder of the glass of water on it, then went over to the equally well upholstered chair opposite.

'Just to ease your mind,' he commented conversationally, 'I've nothing more planned for this evening than to eat the casserole which Mrs Underhill has left in the microwave, and to catch up with some work in my study.'

'Oh,' Bevin murmured and, because she was feeling unexpectedly better all round, she smiled.

She didn't suppose for a minute that her smile had anything to do with it, but, when she'd thought she'd probably be on her way in the next half-hour, he suddenly surprised her by saying, 'If you're exceptionally well behaved, I might consider sharing my casserole with you.'

Although she felt so beaten, Bevin was aware that laughter was tinkling away inside her. 'I don't know your name,' she heard herself say for answer.

'Jarvis Devilliers,' he supplied straight away, and, his eyes asking the same question of her, he inclined his head slightly to one side.

'Bevin Pemberton,' she complied.

'How do you do, Bevin Pemberton?' he said formally, and having been his guest for a good hour, she thought, she was again taken by an urge to laugh. Was it him, something about the man, that made her feel good? she wondered. Or was it just that, having been down for so long, one couldn't stay down for ever? 'You may have a trace more colour in your face, but you're still far from well,' he observed, a moment later, and went on to suggest, 'Why not put your feet up on the couch?'

The idea sounded like heaven, but, 'I've got my shoes on,' she answered primly—and saw that she had amused him.

'Are you always so well-mannered?' he enquired, leaving his chair and coming over to her.

'Invariably,' she replied, and was astounded when he did no more than lift up each foot in turn and remove her shoes. Then as his glance skimmed the pair of ill-fitting man's socks she had on her feet, he moved her until she was resting with her back still against the one end of the couch and her feet were stretched out on the couch in front of her. 'My father's—the socks, I mean,' she explained of the unglamorous thick grey covering. 'I—er—thought I'd better dress warmly today, so...'

'You live with your father?' Jarvis Devilliers enquired, as he returned to his seat, his expression serious, and Bevin realised his question was because of his earlier comment that plainly she had no one to care for her, yet, by the look of it, her father must live in the same house, or how did she have access to his socks?

Her expression was serious too as she revealed quietly, 'My father died three weeks ago.'

'I'm sorry,' he said, and Bevin warmed to him that his tone was not falsely sympathetic but sounding as if he too knew what it was like to lose some close family member. 'You were fond of him,' he stated, not questioning, but as though from the few words she'd spoken of her parent, he had gleaned as a fact that she was fond of her father.

'You understand,' she murmured huskily, and asked, 'Have you lost someone recently too?'

'My grandfather died six months ago,' he stated briefly, and Bevin intuitively knew that he and his grandfather had been very close—and also that he did not wish to speak about it.

Suddenly she felt sensitive to his feelings, so she quickly brought the subject away from his loss to go on to tell him, just as if his statement about her being fond of her father had been a question, 'My father could be a bit—crusty—at times, but I loved him.'

'And you're missing him.' She nodded, and Jarvis went on, 'You're not living with your mother?'

'She died when I was eleven.'

'So you live alone?' he probed, his tone gentle, sympathetic to her loneliness—and all at once Bevin started to feel guilty. She had no right to his sympathy, and she suddenly felt she had to explain what, if asked, she would have said she could never reveal to any of the people she knew—much less to a stranger. Oliver Taylor was the exception in that he'd happened along while she was still reeling from the

shock of Mr Ford telling her that Irene had a better
claim to her father's estate than she had.

'No,' she replied, just the one word as she waded
through a fog of wondering how to explain something
she still found baffling.

'No?' he queried, quite mildly, she realised, when
he could well be conjecturing just what she thought
she was doing in accepting his hospitality, his min-
istrations, when, despite all signs to the contrary, she
had someone in her own home who could look after
her.

'It—I...' She looked over to him, saw he was
waiting, and swallowed painfully, realised that all she
needed was swollen glands to complete the set, and
looked away to tell him despondently, 'I *thought* I
was going to live alone. In fact, I did for about a week
after my father died, but...' she paused to cough,
almost panicked that she was about to start off on a
prolonged bout again, but to her relief didn't, and
began again. 'My father married again when I was
fourteen.'

'How long ago was that?' her kind host enquired,
seeming to be a man who liked to document his facts
as he went along.

'Eight years ago,' she replied. 'But the marriage
didn't work out, and about a year later Irene, his new
wife, moved out again.'

'You're saying she's moved back in again?' Bevin
blinked—was he quick or was he quick! She nodded.
'You contacted her—saw her at the funeral, perhaps—
and asked her to come back?' he suggested.

'No!' she denied. 'Irene didn't attend my father's
funeral! I'd seen nothing of her for years, then the
day after the funeral she came to the house saying

that my father's bank account was frozen and saying she wanted her allowance.'

'She expected you to give it to her?'

'I'm not sure. We never got down to that because she was suddenly asking about my father's will.'

Bevin had no idea why she was telling him any of this, and halted suddenly. Though, when she looked across at Jarvis Devilliers, she saw that his expression had gone so stern that she almost asked him what was wrong. Before she could do so, however, he was dismissing whatever had been going through his mind and his expression became somewhat warmer as he took up, 'Let me guess. She wanted to know what your father had left her.'

'Yes,' Bevin said huskily, then discovered that Jarvis had misread the situation.

'And you were able to tell her that he'd left her the house—and she immediately moved in.'

'You're right in the one part in that she moved in the very next day, but although I didn't see the will until Irene set about looking for it, the house and everything else had been left unconditionally to me.'

'You invited your stepmother to move in?' he enquired, seeming surprised, having gathered, she realised, that there was no love lost between her and her stepmother.

'She didn't have to wait for an invitation. She took a copy of the will to her solicitors and discovered that it was so badly worded—and my solicitor confirmed it when I checked it out—that she can claim everything!'

'Ye gods! Didn't your father have his will legally drawn up?' he asked, astounded.

Bevin coughed, felt miserable, but had to confess, 'While he could be very generous sometimes, my father was at others most—er—thrifty.'

'To the extent that his thrift lost you your inheritance,' Jarvis documented.

But while it had been she who had mentioned her father's thrift, it did not sit well with Bevin to hear someone who had neither known nor loved him talk of her father's thrift, in this case, as if it were a fault. Which left her, since talk of and around her father had been the topic for some while, to think of something else to say. She found it in the question, 'Are you a lawyer?'

He shook his head, but to her relief, strangely, as if aware of all her thoughts and feelings, he allowed her to leave the subject under discussion, and replied, 'No to doctor, no to lawyer,' and, with a friendly look, 'I work for Devilliers, the engineering science group.'

'Oh, I've heard of them!' she suddenly remembered, and tried to think what it was she'd heard about the big conglomerate. 'Haven't they just won a massive order for some work abroad?' she pulled out of a vague nowhere.

'We were fortunate. But,' without false modesty, 'we're good.'

Bevin smiled tiredly. Then, more alertly, 'But *your* name's Devilliers!' she suddenly woke up to realise.

'True,' he agreed.

Her mouth fell open, and, as she thought of the sheer size of the firm, she gasped, 'Do you run it?'

'I have some help,' he replied, and, when from shock or she knew not what she sucked in breath, she brought on a spate of coughing which she just could not control, Jarvis was off his chair and over by the head of the settee doing what he could to help her. 'I've exhausted you with my questioning,' he muttered when her coughing at last subsided, then he handed her the glass of water from the small table. 'Rest now,' he instructed, 'while I go and do things brilliant with the microwave.'

Feeling worn out, Bevin leant back and looked at the well-to-do business man who had taken charge of her when she had all but collapsed in the street—and who, when he was under no obligation whatsoever, had not left it there.

'You've so very kind,' she told him huskily, and felt warmed through and through again when he gave her a twisted kind of a grin.

'I know—I can't understand it!' he commented lightly. Then, getting down to matters serious, 'From the look of you I'd say you haven't the strength to sit at the dining table. I'll bring you a tray,' he decided. And before she could protest that she didn't want to put him to any trouble, he was telling her practically where his bathroom was should she want to wash her hands before her meal.

Her gratitude to him was endless as in her woollen-sock-clad feet she pattered to the bathroom and returned to the couch. He really was a wonderful man, she thought, and with her feet up on the couch again, she closed her eyes.

She felt dreadfully tired, and yet, at the same time, given the mental anguish she'd been through recently, she felt more at peace within herself than she had since her father died. She adjusted her position on the couch, and her body ached, so she moved some more until she found a really comfortable position.

Suddenly, however, her temperature started to soar and she began to feel hot. It was comfortable on the couch, though, but all the same, she didn't want her sweater on. Her aching body protested as she took her sweater off, but she felt better once she'd dropped it to the floor. Better too once she'd taken the socks from her burning feet.

In fact, she thought hazily as she settled down again in her comfortable position, she felt better about everything suddenly. Even better about the fact that Irene had inherited the house. Perhaps it did one good to talk about these things, she thought tiredly and, completely used up, she fell fast asleep.

A bout of coughing woke her up some time around two in the morning. Though for some reason she felt no alarm to find she was trouser and shirt-clad and had fallen asleep on someone else's couch. The fact that there was a small shaded light gently illuminating part of the room, and that a cream-coloured soft fleecy blanket was over her, might be responsible for soothing any anxiety she felt to wake up in a strange sitting-room, she realised vaguely. But, her endless coughing taking up most of her energy, she felt in no way alarmed either when a tall robe-clad figure appeared out of nowhere and instructed, 'Drink this.'

'Thank you,' she murmured from a hoarse throat, and aching all over, she fell back into her comfortable couch—and went to sleep again.

Dawn was breaking when next she woke, and the tall man was there again. This time, though, he was shaved and dressed. 'How are you feeling?' he asked.

Bevin fought a battle between politeness and truth. Politeness won. 'Fine,' she replied, and struggled to sit up.

Clearly she was not believed, but she was glad she had lied when, looking amused, 'You know, I could get to like you, Bevin Pemberton,' the man remarked, then instructed, 'Sit tight, I'll get you a cup of tea.'

Bevin sat tight, but by the time he came back she was remembering, and going through agonies because of it, all the things she had confided in him last night. True, he had asked a pertinent question or two as, she realised, a man in his position, a man who ran a company as large as Devilliers, would have to. Grief, she thought suddenly, for all he knew she might be the sort of female who would love to make capital of his kindness, his generosity, and invent some story that would ensure his name being dragged through the tabloids!

Bevin pushed the cover of the blanket away from her in some anxiety, then as she realised that Jarvis Devilliers must be a better judge of character than to bring any predatory female into his apartment, she pulled the blanket back around her.

But, while she felt a small glow that Jarvis had judged—as he'd asked her to trust him—that he in turn could trust her, Bevin was wondering, had she really told him all she had? Had she perhaps been a trifle delirious? Had she in fact dreamt it?

A moment later, though, she was staring down at the cream fleecy blanket as though for the first time. Had Jarvis, making sure she wouldn't be cold during the night, really covered her over with a blanket? And, good heavens, what was she thinking of, had she *really* spent the night on his couch?

'I should have gone home!' she told him urgently, the moment he appeared with a cup of tea.

Unhurriedly, he set her tea down on the table near her and came and sat on the edge of the couch, his all-assessing grey-blue gaze taking in her tousled red-blonde hair, her flushed cheeks, and the fact that her lovely brown eyes revealed that she was still far from well. 'What brought that on?' he questioned.

'I should have. It wasn't fair to you,' she replied.

'Forget that for a moment,' he instructed, 'and tell me truthfully: do you regret staying here last night?'

It didn't take very much thinking about. Especially when she recalled how much better she had felt about everything since she had been in his home. How much more at peace she had felt within herself since she had been in his home. She thought of her home, the home that, since Irene had moved in, had become a cheerless place and, as truthfully as Jarvis had asked her, 'No,' she told him, 'I don't regret staying here.'

For some long moments after receiving her answer, Jarvis Devilliers continued to stare thoughtfully at her as though considering some matter in depth. But, when it seemed he had just come to a decision, all he said as he got to his feet was 'Drink your tea, Bevin,' and, as her startled eyes followed him, he strode purposefully from the room.

To decide to tell her to drink her tea didn't seem much of a decision to have to make, she thought light-headedly. But her throat seemed parched, so she drank the hot liquid and, while trying to pretend she didn't feel so very dreadful, wished very much that she felt better. Where she was going to find the energy from to walk the long length of her garden path once the taxi had dropped her off—and, since Jarvis had done more than his fair share as it was, she'd insist on taking a taxi—she didn't know.

She'd get off the couch and go in a minute, she decided, but she'd started to feel muzzy-headed again. She closed her eyes for a brief while—and woke to find Jarvis Devilliers standing there looking down at her.

She had thought he was looking quite agreeable, but when he bluntly stated, 'You can't stay there like that!' more colour came to her face, and she felt worse than she had ever done in her life.

'I'll just get my sweater on...' she responded hurriedly, and moving quickly, too quickly in her pride, she went to stand up—and had only just got to her feet when she had to clutch at him for support. But proudly she pushed away from him, and proudly she began, 'I was just leaving...' only he cut her short.

'Don't be absurd,' he rapped. 'You're not fit to go anywhere!' And, while realising that she must have got something wrong, and she stood there rockily trying to comprehend what it was he meant, he caught her by the shoulders and moved her to sit back on the couch while he went on, 'Apart from the fact that you've coughed the night away and are completely debilitated, you've got a roaringly high temperature.'

'I'll be all right when I get home and into bed,' she insisted.

'You're right about the bed bit—only I don't see how I can possibly allow you to go home!' he told her forthrightly.

Her head was throbbing to beat the band, and again she tried hard for comprehension, but it was no use. 'I'm not with you,' she had to confess.

'Is it likely that your stepmother will bring you so much as a warm drink once you get back there?' he questioned. From the experience she'd so far had,

Bevin felt it more likely that Irene would be peeved
that she wasn't making dinner for her, and unhappily
she shook her head. 'I thought not,' Jarvis muttered,
and with an encouraging look at her defeated face,
'Which is why I've just made up a bed in my guest
bedroom.'

The look of defeat left her expression as she stared
at him disbelievingly. 'You want me to stay here?' she
questioned, but, as she immediately realised that he
couldn't *want* anything of the sort, 'You mean I *can*
stay here?' she rephrased it, and supposed there must
have been something in her look which gave away that
the idea of getting into bed without too much delay
had tremendous merit as far as she was concerned.
For, the next she knew, Jarvis Devilliers was helping
her to her feet.

'Come on,' he was ordering, and as if to make her
feel better, 'I knew those pyjamas my sister gave me
for Christmas would be of some use,' he teased, and
while Bevin was hazily taking in that he must prefer
to sleep pyjamaless and that he had a sister, he was
guiding her from the sitting-room and along the hall
and through to a bedroom, complete with its own
bathroom. It was in the bedroom that he sat her on
the bed and, pointing to the pyjamas newly taken out
of their cellophane wrapper, and the freshly laundered robe alongside them, he instructed kindly, and
just as though she was about ten years old, 'Get into
bed, poppet, while I go and rustle you up something
to eat.'

'I don't want to be a nuisance,' she told him jerkily.

'That's good,' he replied lightly, and left her.

Bevin was not conscious of where most of that day
went. Jarvis brought her some scrambled egg, which

she ate and promptly fell fast asleep. Then a coughing bout woke her a couple of hours later.

She was sitting up trying to find some relief when, carrying a spoon and a proprietary brand of cough medicine, Jarvis suddenly came into the room. 'According to the pharmacist, the world and his wife have gone down with a particularly virulent strain of flu bug that's going around,' he informed her as he matter-of-factly poured some of the linctus into the spoon.

'Oh, I hope you don't get it!' she exclaimed.

'I'll sue you if I do,' Jarvis told her pleasantly, and took advantage of her open mouth to tip the medicine in. 'Do you need a sweet?' he asked. And, while she admitted to feeling quite a long way below par, there was just something about him that had her laughing. 'You'll do,' he commented, as the husky sound of a light laugh left her, and he waited a while to see if she was going to start coughing again, then suggested, 'You'll probably feel better if you lie down again,' and when she obeyed he pulled the covers up around her, and quietly left her to her healing sleep.

The next time she awoke, it was on hearing the outer door of the apartment close as someone let themselves in. Only then did it dawn on her that Jarvis must have gone out earlier to fetch her some cough medicine—had he been out again?

She realised that he had when a short while later he came in with a tray of fish and chips. 'Oh, Jarvis,' she mourned, 'I'm putting you to an awful lot of trouble.'

'Nonsense!' he said briskly. 'I have to eat myself— it was no trouble to ask for two helpings.'

'Do you usually have fish and chips for lunch on a Saturday?'

'It has been known,' he returned, but confided, 'Working on the "feed a cold, starve a fever" principle, it occurred to me that a load of carbohydrates might not come amiss. Think you can manage some stodge?'

'It looks delicious,' she smiled.

She slept a lot that afternoon, but woke up feeling strangely troubled. She sat up in bed, and while she glanced round the expensive but solid-looking furniture, everything seemed to be unreal. She was aware, though, that she couldn't be delirious, but realised she must be quite a bit light-headed, in that it seemed to be disturbing her that she hadn't let Irene know where she was.

She shrugged the notion away—as if Irene would care where she was, for goodness' sake! She closed her eyes, but she had slept enough, and she couldn't rest. A minute went by, and then another, and then Bevin decided she felt very much better. She was sure of it when, getting out of bed, she found she didn't feel anywhere near as rocky on her feet as she had done.

She spotted the towelling robe at the bottom of the bed and put it on. It was big, the pyjamas were big. She was fairly tall herself, long-legged, but the pyjama bottoms still flapped round her feet. She sat down and rolled them back a few turns, and then, still plagued by thoughts of Irene, went barefoot from her room.

Jarvis had heard her moving about, she realised, for as she entered the sitting-room, he came through a door on the other side. If he had taken in in that first all-seeing gaze that she still had something of a temperature, he did not comment on it, but enquired mildly, 'Stretching your legs?'

'Do you think I should ring my stepmother?' she asked.

'No, I don't,' he said, his eyes steady on her. 'But if it's going to worry you, you can come into my study and call her.'

'You're working!' Bevin exclaimed as he guided her through the door he had just come from.

'Just finishing off a few things,' he remarked. 'Nothing too important.' That last was said to make her feel better for interrupting him, Bevin felt. 'What number?' he enquired, and she realised that since she had interrupted him now, she might as well make the call.

She told him her home number and he stabbed out the digits, then passed the phone over to her, and she didn't mind at all that he stayed close by. She had forgotten, though, what a loud voice her stepmother had, and automatically pulled the phone away from her ear as Irene's amplified voice hit her eardrums. 'Hello!'

'Hello, Irene, it's Bevin,' she began as she recovered. 'I'm ringing to tell you that I'll be back soon, but that . . .'

'Huh! I thought you'd got the message,' Irene bellowed nastily, 'and moved out permanently!' With that, she banged the phone back on the receiver, and Bevin, who was aware that Jarvis must have heard every word, was left standing there feeling ashamed, hurt, and utterly miserable.

She flicked a glance at him as he stretched out a hand and took the phone from her, but as their eyes met she bit her lip and, utterly embarrassed, looked quickly away.

But, as if seeing her hurt, Jarvis was suddenly reaching for her, and was holding her, cradling her to him, her head against his chest—and if she was delirious, or was dreaming, then she never wanted to wake up. Because, from feeling lost, miserable and unhappy, never had she known such comfort.

Though when she all at once sagged limply against him, 'Come on, back to bed,' he instructed quietly. Then, when she just didn't feel like moving, he followed through by gently picking her up in his arms and, as if she weighed nothing at all, carrying her back to her room.

CHAPTER THREE

NEITHER Bevin nor her host slept very much that night, for she was awake half the night coughing. 'I'm sorry,' she apologised yet again when Jarvis left his bed around three on Sunday morning. 'I could have done that myself,' she protested weakly as he popped another spoonful of linctus into her mouth.

'Are you trying to make me redundant?' he asked mock-severely, and Bevin felt she really liked him. In her view, disturbed and brought from his bed by her incessant coughing, he was being remarkably even-tempered.

The linctus settled her for a while, but she was awake again at dawn and doing her best to stifle the sounds of her harsh cough. But Jarvis heard her, though this time when he came in, he had obviously given up all hope of getting any rest, for, where earlier there had been a fair amount of stubble on his chin and he had been wearing a robe, he was now clean-shaven and dressed.

'I'm going home,' she told him decisively, if glumly, aware that he could only welcome such news.

Strangely, though, he didn't look anywhere near as ecstatic as she had imagined. In fact, if anything, he looked very much put out. 'Do you think that's fair to me?' he enquired sharply.

'I—don't understand,' she said in a hoarse voice she was getting used to.

'After two nights of my fantastic nursing, you'd put your recovery in jeopardy by returning to an in-hospitable place where we both know in advance you'll get no nursing at all!' he rebuked her. And suddenly, at his goodness, at the truth of what he had said—albeit she had espied a definite twinkle in his eyes when he'd spoken of his fantastic nursing—Bevin felt weak and weepy.

'Oh, Jarvis!' she wailed, as her decisiveness departed.

'Hush now,' he soothed, and propped her up on her pillows.

From then on for the next few hours he was either coming in to her room to bring her something to eat or something to drink or to just generally check on her.

It was around ten-thirty that morning, however, when her temperature had begun to soar again, that Jarvis came back into her room. Bevin guessed it must have been pretty evident that she wasn't feeling so good when, possessing no thermometer, Jarvis moved casually over to the bed and placed a cool hand on her burning forehead.

'Straight up, how do you feel?' he questioned, his tone serious and warning her that he didn't want to hear 'Fine' for an answer.

'There have been days when I've felt more like tackling a game of tennis,' she wheezed, and when he took his cool hand away from her forehead she wanted it back again.

She drifted off into a restless sleep when he had gone, and was dreaming quarrelsome dreams as she came to the surface of wakefulness again where her

conscience was telling her she must leave, and Jarvis
Devilliers was saying she must say.

She opened her eyes just as the door, which had
been left ajar, was pushed further open, and Jarvis
came in again. But he did not come in alone, for he
had an attractive woman of about thirty with him and,
strangely, Bevin experienced the most extraordinary
feeling of depression that no doubt his woman friend
was a regular Sunday visitor to his home.

She started to feel awful that she was taking up his
guest bedroom, and she had no idea—although the
woman seemed to be smiling most kindly at her—how
his friend felt about it. Then Bevin suddenly discovered that she had no need to feel awkward in any
degree. 'This is Bevin Pemberton,' Jarvis told his
friend and, turning his attention to the flushed-
cheeked strawberry blonde in the bed, 'Bevin, this is
Cheryl Todd.' He paused, then added, 'Dr Cheryl
Todd.'

Bevin's mouth fell open, and only then did she
notice that the woman's over-large handbag was not
in fact a handbag at all, but could easily be a doctor's
bag—the type that housed a stethoscope.

'You haven't . . .' she began to protest.

'I have,' he replied, and neatly cutting off further
protests before she could make them, 'Do you want
me to stay while Dr Todd examines you?'

Bevin's reply was instinctive and immediate. 'No!'
she told him—he grinned, and disappeared, and
Cheryl Todd moved nearer to the bed and put down
her bag.

'Mr Devilliers has told me a little about you,' she
smiled. 'Do you mind if I ask you a few more
questions?'

Ten minutes later Bevin had answered several pleasantly put questions, had been stethoscoped back and front, and Cheryl Todd, after telling her that what she needed was some sound rest, was administering an injection. Bevin felt too woolly-headed to ask what the injection was going to do, but she had no objection to make. The doctor did not stay long, and while Bevin was thanking her, she began packing up her bag, and a minute later she smiled, and left the room.

Bevin realised that Jarvis must be in conversation with the doctor, for she could hear but not make out what they were saying. They could have been talking in lowered tones, she realised, because suddenly she *could* make out what they were saying when, just as the outer door opened, she heard Jarvis say, 'I'll call you again if need be.'

'Of course,' the doctor agreed, 'but it shouldn't be necessary.'

It hadn't been necessary in the first place, Bevin thought, and felt guilty again at the trouble she was putting everyone to. Then she heard the sound of Jarvis coming to see her, so she struggled up out of a general feeling of tiredness to pin what she could in the way of a smile on her face, and to ask as his tall fair-headed length came through the door, 'Will I live?'

'If you do as you're told,' he replied easily, as Bevin began again to have conscience trouble.

'I hope Dr Todd didn't mind being called out on a Sunday,' she began fretfully. 'She must be rushed off her feet as it is with so much flu about, without...'

'Cheryl Todd isn't in general practice,' Jarvis cut in to state, and at Bevin's puzzled look, 'She's the works doctor who happens to live just a mile or two away,' he filled in. And while Bevin was thinking, the poor woman, she wasn't even on call but had had her Sunday interrupted anyway, he was going on. 'And, as I began to suspect, you've a little more the matter with you than flu.'

'I have?' she exclaimed. 'What's the...'

'You, little Bevin,' he told her, when she was all of five feet eight, 'are suffering from a flu-type illness brought on by delayed shock. The two combined have flattened you.'

She stared at him in stupefaction. 'I'm in delayed shock—from my father's death and all that's happened since?' she questioned, somehow needing his help to get it straight in her head.

'That seems about it,' he agreed, but smiled reassuringly and continued, 'Though, given that you need to rest and not to worry about a thing, and given that we get you started on the medicines Cheryl has prescribed—the good news is that by tomorrow you should be showing signs of tremendous improvement.'

Her, 'Thank goodness for that!' came from the heart.

'Now, according to Cheryl, she's given you something that should knock you out for a while. Are you going to be good while I go and collect your prescription?'

She loved his teasing; it made her feel better that here she was again putting him to the trouble of going to the chemist's. 'Yes,' she said meekly, and smiled, and closed her eyes.

She heard him go out, and was half asleep when almost at once she heard him come back again. That was, she heard him ringing the door bell and realised that clearly he had forgotten something. It could only be his key, she realised sleepily. He must have come back for it straight away rather than leave it until after he'd collected her prescription, when, had the injection taken full effect, she might be sound asleep and he might never get her to answer the door.

He rang the bell again, for longer this time, and Bevin dragged herself out of bed, guessing he was urgently trying to wake her up. She found she was shaky on her legs, but she eventually made it to the outer door of the flat, and then had a problem in turning the door catch. But she managed it at last, and pulled the door back, to find that—it wasn't Jarvis!

A tall fair-haired woman stood there, and looked as startled to see Bevin as Bevin was to see her. Vaguely Bevin thought the woman must be about the same age as Cheryl Todd, but that was where the similarity ended, for this woman had a look of arrogance about her, and didn't sound in the least friendly. 'Well, well, well, who are you?' she wanted to know.

'Bevin Pemberton,' Bevin replied, but felt so drowsy that she wasn't at all sure what to say next.

Then she found she was required to say very little, for, giving her pyjamas and flushed cheeks the once-over, the fair-haired woman remarked, 'It seems I've called at an inconvenient time,' and Bevin fought off waves of sleep and tried to pull herself together.

'Who are you?' she enquired from her hoarse throat, as she somehow realised she had better find that out first before she invited the woman in.

'I'm Jarvis's sister, but I won't stay,' the woman replied, and was already turning away, when Bevin got herself more together.

'Jarvis won't...' she began, but found she was talking to the air.

She closed the door and went back to her bed wondering what it was she had been going to say. 'Jarvis won't...' but for the life of her she couldn't remember.

She didn't hear him come back in, and in fact, except for Jarvis waking her up now and then to either feed her or give her some medication, she seemed to sleep most of the day.

To her surprise, she slept solidly all through Sunday night as well, and woke up early on Monday morning to hear rain lashing against the windows and to find Jarvis, business-suited, standing over her with more medication in his hands. There was also a cup of tea on her bedside table, and a tray of what looked like something to eat under its cover on another table which he had brought into the room.

'Good morning,' she greeted him, and was pleasantly surprised to find that her throat no longer hurt.

'How's the head?' he asked.

'Fine,' she replied, and he let her get away with it, and instructed her on the frequency with which she should take her medication.

'Stay in bed,' he went on to order, 'and...'

'You don't think I should leave today?' she asked worriedly—and saw at once from his change of expression that her question had not gone down very well.

'Are you deliberately trying to annoy me?' he barked shortly, and Bevin did not at all like the stern autocrat he had suddenly become.

'I don't think I've got the energy,' she retorted with what spirit she could muster—and felt ridiculously happier when the harsh look abruptly left him and, his expression suddenly rueful, he came and sat down on the edge of her bed.

'Are you going to forgive me because fear that you'll earn yourself pneumonia if you go out into the downpour going on outside brought out the brute in me?' he asked, and caused her skin to tingle when he absently caught hold of one of her pale hands lying on the coverlet.

'I'll try,' she answered solemnly, and saw an amused look enter his grey-blue eyes.

'But you'll promise to stay put?' he asked, and there was suddenly such charm in him that Bevin weakly felt she would promise him anything when he was like this.

'Yes,' she said simply, but wished she'd pulled herself more together, because as he returned her hand to the coverlet, then stood up and went off to his office, she was sure there was something she wanted to tell him—though for the life of her she couldn't remember what it was.

She spent the morning sleeping and waking and taking her medicines in the prescribed doses, and it was around two o'clock in the afternoon that she suddenly realised she was beginning to feel very much better. Her headache had gone, she was coughing very much less, ached less, and she felt certain her temperature was well down. She flicked a glance at the bathroom—and began to yearn to take a bath.

Half an hour later the yearning grew too large to handle. Deciding not to rush things, Bevin got out of bed and, pleased to find that she felt far steadier on her feet than she had for the last couple of days, she padded to the bathroom.

While her bath was filling she rinsed through her underwear and rolled it in a towel to dry, and then, shedding her over-large pyjamas, 'Ah, paradise!' she murmured, and soaked for an age in a warm bath.

The temperature in the apartment was constant, but, feeling a little chilled after she had dried herself and donned her pyjamas, Bevin got back into bed and, feeling tired again, but pleasantly so, and not so utterly exhausted as she had been, she dropped off to sleep once more.

It was dark when she awoke, but putting on the bedside light, she saw from her watch that it was only a little after six. Suddenly she felt thirsty and wondered if she should go and find the kitchen and make herself a cup of tea. She had no idea what time Jarvis would be home, but realised that since no one running a company would put his pen down on the stroke of five, realised too that it could be quite some time before she saw him again.

With her need for a cup of tea decreeing that she couldn't wait that long to ask Jarvis for permission to make free with his kitchen, Bevin got up, certain he wouldn't mind. Donning her robe and taking her tray of used dishes with her, flicking lights on as she went, she entered the hall and went into the sitting-room and over to the door which she had several times seen him use.

She found the kitchen without any problem, but realised that Jarvis hadn't been joking when he'd said she'd caught him on a good day and that the state of his apartment got progressively worse until his cleaning lady's next visit. The sitting-room had been tidy, but the kitchen, although not too bad, showed signs of being used by someone who knew little about kitchen duties, and who had no desire to learn.

Setting the kettle to boil, Bevin ran some hot water into a bowl, found some washing-up liquid and set to work washing up the tray of dishes she had brought with her, and also one or two other oddments of used china she found lying around. She had just finished wiping down some work surfaces when she heard the sound of Jarvis's key in the door.

She heard him open the door and heard it thud shut behind him, then, when she didn't hear him come into the sitting-room, she realised he had gone straight to his guest bedroom. A smile curved her lovely mouth to think that his first action had been to go along to check how she was, and she hurriedly dried her hands and left the kitchen.

She walked into the sitting-room at the same time that he did, and there her smile abruptly faded. For quite plainly as, with a grim expression, Jarvis stared at her, she could not doubt that he was furious about something—and that something, she instinctively knew, was nothing as innocent as her being out of bed when he'd told her to stay put. Or the fact that, having come from the kitchen, she had been making free use of his home.

'What's—wrong?' she asked chokily, as they neared each other and were separated by only about two yards of carpet. 'What...?'

'You're pretending you don't know?' he snarled.

'I've no idea!' she exclaimed, feeling totally lost—though she did not have to wait much longer for enlightenment.

For suddenly, whatever had been steaming away inside him all the way home from his office broke free. 'The last call I took today was one from my sister,' he rapped, and, as something all at once clicked in Bevin's head, 'Why the *hell* didn't you tell me she called here yesterday?' he slammed into her.

'I'm sorry,' Bevin immediately apologised as she suddenly realised that the thing she'd known that morning she had to tell him, but couldn't then remember, was suddenly recalled. 'She called when you...' she broke off; he knew that anyway. 'I forgot,' she said honestly. 'My head's been a bit cotton-woolly and...'

'Too true it's been cotton-woolly,' he grated. 'Or...' he paused, then went on deliberately, 'Or did I get you wrong?'

'Wrong?' she queried, with no idea what he meant.

He did not leave her in the dark for long, but his very tone was insulting. 'Did I get you wrong, and miss the fact that you're just another female on the make?' he challenged harshly.

Bevin's breath drew in at the cruelty of it, at the pain that hit her that he could say such a thing to her. Then she felt furious, and she wasn't thinking then, but acting. Had she the energy, she felt she would have hit him, but energy was something which she had in short supply just then—and she needed every ounce she could spare to get out of there.

With her fury giving her strength, however, she stormed past him to her room. Never had she been so blisteringly angry. That he—he, the man she liked and respected so much, could say such a thing to her! Well, he could get lost for a start!

Yanking her shirt, trousers and sweater from off a chair, Bevin tossed them on to the bed while she hunted up her socks and shoes. By the time she had remembered that her underwear was still drying in the bathroom, though, her spurt of energy had been used up, and she realised she had company.

'Now what are you doing?' Jarvis Devilliers demanded.

There were several answers which sprang to mind, but her fury had come down from its peak, and was now tempered with pure breeding. 'Thank you very much for your hospitality, Mr Devilliers,' she began formally, but saw, while his fury seemed to have subsided too, that he nevertheless didn't look too enamoured by what she was saying.

'You're thinking of going somewhere?' he grunted.

Was there any doubt! 'After what you've just said, you imagine I'd stay?' she fumed, wishing he'd go so she could go and retrieve her underwear.

'So maybe I was wrong,' he conceded.

'There's no *maybe* about it!' she flared.

'So forgive me,' he suddenly relented, but although his charm was a potent force she just stood there staring stubbornly at him. 'Cheryl Todd would have a fit if I let you go out into the cold night air,' he suddenly announced, and when Bevin was certain it wouldn't bother him a hoot if Cheryl Todd did have a fit, 'Look at you, you're all flushed—you've still got a temperature.'

'That's not temperature—that's temper!' Bevin snapped, and saw amusement she didn't want to see enter his eyes, and worse, felt a matching amusement she didn't want to feel begin to stir in her.

'I somehow never thought of you as having such a fiery temper,' he murmured.

'Until I met you, I didn't,' she answered, and suddenly, as his mouth began to pick up at the corners, the corners of her mouth began to pick up too. And, against all odds a short while ago, suddenly they were both grinning.

'So you'll stay?' he asked.

'Oh, Jarvis,' she said weakly, and turned away, not wanting to go, not now when it was clear that he hadn't really meant what he'd said about her being on the make. Maybe his sister had needled him about her being there and he hadn't liked it—who knew what went on in families?

'That sounds more encouraging than the "Mr Devilliers" I was to you a minute or two back,' he said over her shoulder, and while her smile peeped out again at his teasing, his charm was suddenly there in abundance as he stated pleasantly, 'I do have a peace-offering.'

'Peace-offering?' she questioned, as she turned to face him.

'Wait there,' he ordered, and disappeared momentarily to return with his briefcase, which he opened and withdrew from its crammed interior a paper package. 'One pair of gent's pyjamas—small size,' he announced, passing the parcel over to her.

'You've bought me some pyjamas?' she asked, amazed by his thoughtfulness when he was such a busy man.

'Since you don't know me all that well, I thought you might be happier in those rather than something frilly,' he declared. There was no end to his thoughtfulness, she realised, as she comprehended that, expecting it to be a few more days before she could leave her bed, he had thoughtfully bought her a change of bedwear.

'Oh, Jarvis!' she repeated—and had to laugh.

She stilled, though, when suddenly she caught his glance steady on her mouth. Her laughter died, and quite unexpectedly there seemed to be tension in the air. Then his glance went from her mouth and he stared into her eyes. As though striving to break a tension that he too was aware of, he enquired, 'Did anyone ever tell you that you've got the most beautiful nose?'

'No,' she replied, her voice husky, and she hoped he thought that it was husky from the flu, because suddenly she wasn't at all sure.

'Take my word for it,' he stated. 'You've got a beautiful nose—with just the prettiest shade of glowing pink. The "flu factor", I think it's called.' She laughed, she just had to—he had that effect on her. But, having teased all tension away, 'Hungry?' he enquired.

'A bit,' she replied politely, suddenly feeling ravenous.

'I'll go and heat up something from the freezer,' he remarked as he moved towards the door. Though when he reached the doorway, he stopped. 'If you haven't used up all your energy in learning that you've got a fearsome temper, perhaps you'd like to join me in the dining-room for half an hour?'

Bevin liked the idea. 'Er—dress formal?' she enquired.

'Come as you are,' he lobbed back, and went on his way whistling a snatch of a tune.

Bevin went to tidy her hair—she felt quite light-hearted too.

CHAPTER FOUR

THE weather was still atrocious when Bevin woke the next morning. As well as torrents of rain beating against the window-panes, it now had a companion of howling wind. Thank goodness she didn't have to go out in it, she thought fleetingly, then realised with a shock that of course she had to go out in it! What had she been thinking about? She had a job to do!

She sat up and switched on the bedside lamp. It was still early, so she had no need to rush around yet, she realised, so she leaned back against the headboard, and came to the conclusion that she *must* have been poorly to have forgotten all about her job. She was feeling heaps better now, though, and could not help but again be anxious not to get a reputation for unreliability.

Sounds of Jarvis moving around distracted her, and while she felt she would like to have got up and made him his tea or coffee for a change, she did not want to get in his way if he had things off to a fine art first thing in the morning.

He'd been a superb companion at dinner last night, she recalled, and remembered how they'd conversed on any subject that came up, and how he had seemed genuinely interested in her views and opinions. For herself, she had found him extremely interesting to listen to, and could have stayed listening to him for hours. But when the meal was over she felt that all-seeing gaze of his on her, and when he commented,

'You've done well,' somehow, in tune with him, she knew he was saying it was time she was back in bed.

Not wishing to outstay her welcome, she bade him, 'Goodnight,' and returned to her room.

The sound of Jarvis coming along the hall brought her out of her brief reverie, and, because she liked him, she had a smile on her face when he entered her room, a tray in his hands.

'Oh, Jarvis, you shouldn't!' she protested.

'Ah, you're getting better,' he responded.

'I am. Much, much better,' she declared, and confessed, 'And feeling guilty that you're using your time waiting on me when I shall be getting up in a minute.'

'You *are* feeling better,' he agreed, but went on, 'Though I'd have said a few more days in bed wouldn't be any too many after the exhausting time you've been through.'

'I can't stay in bed that long!' she exclaimed. 'You've been marvellous, you really have,' she rushed on, 'and I'm so grateful. But now I have to leave. I don't know where my head's been since Saturday, but I forgot all about my job. But I must get up and get back to work.'

Jarvis surveyed her sternly from his tall length. 'Ah!' he said again, but this time there was something about the way he said it that caused her to think he knew something that she didn't.

'What...?' she began to question, but suddenly, as if what he had to say would take more than a moment, he came and sat on the edge of her bed. Moving her long legs over to make room for him, Bevin returned her glance to him. 'You were going to say something?' she queried.

'I forgot to tell you,' he obliged, 'you haven't got a job any more.'

Bevin blinked, then felt sure she must have misheard him. 'I—haven't got a job any more?' she repeated, her eyes now glued to his.

He nodded. 'I thought you might want your company to know what was happening, so I rang them.'

'You rang them!' she exclaimed. Her head was much clearer, much smarter than it had been, and she felt certain she hadn't told him who she worked for. 'You don't know who they are!'

'You left your clipboard in my car,' he explained smoothly. 'Their headed notepaper was there for me to see.'

'Oh,' she said faintly, but roused herself to question, a shade unhappily, 'Did they say they didn't want me to continue?'

'Apparently the job was only for a couple of weeks anyway.' He paused, then casually brought out, 'I told them you wouldn't be coming back.'

Astonished by his action, Bevin stared at him open-mouthed. 'You did wh...? But I needed that job!' she protested.

'There are other jobs,' he replied, not seeming to have any idea of how important that job was to her.

'Yes, but I haven't any business qualifications!'

'You need business qualifications to stop passers-by in the street?' he queried, one eyebrow quirking upwards.

'Not just any passer-by,' she got sidetracked. 'You were in my men, professional group, and looked to me to be under forty.'

'Thirty-six,' he supplied, and Bevin realised they had strayed off the point.

'Yes, well, that's just it!' she exclaimed. 'That's why the job is important. I don't *need* business qualifications to do it! Don't you see,' she went on, 'that since I've spent my time since leaving school looking after my father and keeping house, I haven't any work experience outside the home.'

It had been a longish speech, and she coughed and paused for breath, but, when she had thought that Jarvis had comprehended the importance of that job to her, all he said, albeit with a wealth of charm, was, 'Which reminds me, I didn't thank you for smartening up the kitchen for me before I got home yesterday.' Though his expression had gone deadly serious when he went on, 'Which also gives me an idea,' and, while she stared at him with ever-widening eyes, 'Since you haven't got a job to go to—not that it would be on for you anyway in this weather—how do you feel about staying on for another couple of days and cooking me the sort of home-cooked meals that bachelors like me dream of coming home to?'

Joy flooded her heart as she realised that here was a chance not only of putting off the day when she would have to go back to her own home—and Irene—but also of repaying Jarvis in some small measure for his huge kindness.

'You'd like me to cook for you?' she questioned hesitantly.

And was at once put on her mettle when he stipulated, 'Only if you're well enough.'

'What time would you like to eat tonight?' she accepted without further hesitation—and liked him still more when his mouth picked up at the corners.

'How does eight o'clock sound?'

'Bring your appetite home,' she smiled.

'Nothing too elaborate—you're not a hundred per cent fit yet,' he warned.

'Yes, sir,' she laughed, and he stood up and went towards the door.

At the door he turned and looked back at her cheerful smiling face and tousled strawberry-blonde hair tumbling down over her shoulders. 'Don't be in any hurry to get up,' he told her. 'In fact, it might be an idea if you spent the morning in bed.'

'Yes, all right,' she agreed, but was aware as he gave her a distrusting look that he knew as well as she that she had no such intention.

She did have to rest quite a bit that day, though, she found. About half an hour after Jarvis had left for London, she got out of bed and hunted up a washing machine and tumble drier, and put her shirt and pyjamas to wash while she went and had a bath, and washed her hair. Then, in the new pyjamas Jarvis had so thoughtfully brought her, she went and investigated kitchen cupboards and the fridge-freezer.

Ten minutes or so later she came to the conclusion that whatever else Jarvis did in his spare time, it certainly wasn't trying out his hand in the culinary department, because there was barely anything there with which to make a meal.

She supposed she had his cleaning lady-cum-Friday cook, Mrs Underhill, to thank for the fact that there was a stray onion around, and some garlic. Added to that a few oddments of other ingredients, plus some frozen fish, and Bevin reckoned she'd got just about sufficient of everything to make quite a respectable fish curry.

That established, she suddenly felt in the need of a sit-down and accepted then that, even supposing she did still have a job, it would have been the height of folly to have gone out that day and to attempt to do it. She thought that perhaps she should be grateful to Jarvis that, as busy as he must be, he had found time to not only think to get her a change of pyjamas, but also to think to ring her employers. She was finding out for herself what he seemed to know—that she wasn't yet up to standing around waiting for the people she wanted to question to come by. So it had been kind of him, after all, to contact her company to let them know what was happening. Maybe, since everybody got a cold or flu at some time or other, and since Jarvis had done them the courtesy of ringing in, she might be able to approach the same company for work when she felt more up to it. Though that, she suddenly realised grimly, meant when she was back in her old home.

From then until it was time for her to start preparing the meal, Bevin's thoughts went over how in recent years her life had gone on in the same even, not to say dull, fashion, and over and over again on what had happened, much more recently.

It still seemed totally unreal to her that Irene should be able to walk in and claim her home from under her nose. But how much more totally unreal was it that for the last four days she should be occupying the guest bedroom of a man who, until she'd very nearly collapsed on him, had been a total stranger?

Yet Jarvis didn't seem a stranger, and anyhow, nothing seemed real any more. Was it real that the home she had always known should be snatched from her by someone whom her father—whatever his previous feelings—had ended up disliking so very much?

For the moment, though, she acknowledged, she needed some breathing space from the nightmare of it all, and was glad that, in the haven of Jarvis's home, she was afforded time to have that breathing space.

By the time she heard his key in the door that evening, Bevin had changed out of pyjamas and was wearing her own trousers and freshly laundered shirt. 'You look good enough to eat,' he commented, his glance taking in her shining hair and the fact that she had lost her hollow-eyed look. 'And that smell . . .!'

'Curry,' she beamed. 'I'll get the rice started at half-past seven. Er—you're not going out tonight?' the question suddenly popped into her head.

'Trying to get rid of me?' he enquired, looking amused.

'Not at all!' she said, and had to smile, because she was glad he wasn't going out, though she had no idea why she should be—then suddenly she felt a most urgent instinct to get away from such thoughts. She glanced at his briefcase. 'I expect you'll be working in your study later,' she commented.

'I expect I shall,' he agreed pleasantly, and left her to go and freshen up after his day.

Bevin went to busy herself in the kitchen. For some unknown reason—pride, she rather suspected—she wanted the meal she had cooked to be perfect. She realised she might have come close when later, as they sat at the dining-table, Jarvis laid his fork down on a completely cleared plate, and looked across at her.

'That,' he stated, 'rates as one of the best meals I've had in a year.'

'It was all right?' she asked, inwardly glowing.

'Delicious,' he complimented her, and had a question to put himself. 'Now what,' he asked, 'are you going to cook for me tomorrow night?'

Bevin couldn't have been more pleased. He'd meant it, then, when he'd suggested that she stayed on for another couple of days and cooked him some home-cooked meals! 'Um—to be honest, your cupboards and freezer don't hold a lot that I can do too much with,' she felt she had to mention.

'I hadn't thought of that,' he murmured, seeming amused. 'Mrs Underhill takes what she's spent out of her float—it never occurred to me to ask her to stock up.' With his mouth pleasantly curving his look stayed on Bevin as he instructed, 'Give me a list of anything you need, and I'll have it sent in tomorrow.'

'I can shop,' she told him. 'There's no need for you to...'

'Oh, but there is,' he cut her off, and with gentle charm, 'You might be putting up a good front, little Bevin, but no way are you up to lugging baskets of shopping around.' She opened her mouth to disagree, but he got in first. 'I once had flu,' he recalled, 'and felt drained for weeks afterwards.'

She wasn't sure if he was making that last bit up, but since perhaps she might not yet be up to hauling pounds of potatoes and the like back, she swallowed down any protest she might have made and smiled as she conceded, 'So I'll have an early night and leave you to work in your study.'

'Makes us sound quite domesticated,' he remarked good-humouredly.

And why she wasn't sure, probably that word dom-esticated, probably the fact of his good humour, but somehow it seemed more possible for her to bring up a subject which had been restless in the back of her mind ever since he, in fury, had gone for her when he'd come in last night.

'By the way, I did honestly forget that your sister had called here on Sunday while you were out,' she felt obliged to clear up any misconception he might still hold on the matter. Then she wished that she hadn't when all sign of him being amused promptly departed, and Bevin feared he still felt she had 'forgotten' on purpose.

'I know,' he replied quietly, but added, without heat, 'Did I apologise properly for—be it only briefly—thinking otherwise?'

'There's no need for you to apologise,' she answered swiftly. But as she suddenly realised that, for some reason, it must have been important to him to know of his sister's visit—although Bevin didn't think she had left any message, 'I just wanted you to know that I genuinely forgot,' she went on. 'But there was no message to pass on. I'm sure I would have...'

'Don't worry about it,' Jarvis cut in, in such a kindly way that Bevin at once started to feel better.

She smiled across the table at him. 'As long as my forgetting hasn't created a problem,' she commented lightly to end the subject—then found that it wasn't ended.

For although she half expected he might say, No, of course not—he did nothing of the kind. But after a moment's reflection, to her surprise he answered, 'Let's say that a problem which was already in existence has, by Rosalind's seeing you here, been added to.'

Bevin's warm brown eyes widened. 'Oh, I'm so sorry!' she at once declared, and because it concerned

her, even though she couldn't see how she could be
the cause of a problem being added to, she just had
to know more. 'What sort of a problem?' she asked.

For long silent moments Jarvis just sat and studied
her from across the table. But, just when she was beginning to think she was never going to know, and
that he felt the matter was private, he leaned back in
his chair and, with his eyes still on her, replied quietly,
'It seems, Bevin, that you and I have more in common
than either of us knew when you came up to me on
Friday, asked me if I'd mind—and then nearly
crumpled in a heap at my feet.'

That didn't make things any clearer, and although
she could hardly believe that it was only last Friday
that she had met him, she could not help but be very
much intrigued to know what, in this particular in-
stance, they had that was so very much in common.

'What? How?' she enquired.

He shrugged, but this time didn't keep her waiting
for an answer, revealing without further contem-
plation, 'We both, you and I, appear to have come
off at the sticky end of a relative's will.'

'You too?' she asked, in some surprise.

He nodded, going on, 'In your case, your father
left you everything without conditions—though he
didn't get a lawyer to check out the wording. In my
case, my grandfather has left his will so tightly buttoned up that there's no way I—nor the rest of the
family—can claim, unless I comply, before my thirty-
seventh birthday, with one very big condition.'

His grandfather had died six months ago, Bevin recalled Jarvis telling her, and recalled too how she had
instinctively known that he and his grandfather had
been very close. But he had just said that he too had

come off at the sticky end of a relative's will, and she owned to be intrigued to know how, in his case, this was so.

'You're thirty-six now,' she recollected, 'so, by the sound of it, you've got to comply with the—er—big condition in under twelve months, if you and the rest of your family,' she suddenly remembered, 'can claim your inheritance.'

'I've less than five months in which to satisfy the stipulation he laid down,' Jarvis informed her, his expression suddenly sombre. 'Which is why my sister and my parents—my father and Rosalind more particularly—are giving me a lot of trouble.'

'Oh, I'm sorry,' she offered sympathetically, but asked, 'Don't they have to comply with the stipulation too?'

'Hardly,' he replied, adding drily if somewhat obscurely, 'They're both married.' And while she was realising that marriage somehow had something to do with it, Jarvis was going on to tell her, 'My grandfather's marriage was little short of sublime, and with my parents having found the same happy formula, and Rosalind too, Grandfather wanted the same for me.'

'He wants you to have a happy marriage.'

'I think, when I showed more signs of enjoying my bachelor freedom than looking like getting married, he must have got desperate. He didn't state I'd have to have a "happy" marriage,' Jarvis commented drolly, 'just that if the properties and monies weren't to go out of the family, I should be married by my thirty-seventh birthday.'

'Good heavens!' Bevin exclaimed.

'You can say that again!' Jarvis remarked with some feeling. 'My family have been on my neck ever since they knew the terms of Grandfather's will.'

'Because they know that they'll lose their inheritance if you don't acquiesce?'

'As they see it—their rightful inheritance,' he agreed. 'Only *they* aren't the ones who need to give up their freedom to get it.'

From the vague recollection she had of his sister, Bevin had an impression that she had been elegantly and expensively attired, but she wasn't terribly sure of that, and enquired, 'Are they very poor, your family?'

'Good lord, no!' he said unequivocally. 'But that doesn't stop them pleading poverty—as my grandfather knew they would. Just as he knew how, in order to get their hands on what they consider as rightfully theirs, they'd push and push at me to do the "right" thing.'

'Oh, Jarvis,' Bevin commiserated—and she thought her father had left things badly! She guessed then that where what her father had left had seemed to her to be considerable, what Jarvis's grandfather had left well exceeded the term. Suddenly then, though, his sister's visit to his flat on Sunday, her subsequent phone call to Jarvis at his office on Monday, all took on a new meaning to Bevin. 'Oh, heavens!' she cried. 'You'd much prefer your sister hadn't seen me, wouldn't you?'

'She has rather taken heart from seeing you here,' he admitted.

Oh grief, Bevin thought, and the last thing she wanted to give Jarvis was trouble. 'Shall I go?' she offered instantly.

'Be rather like shutting the stable door after the horse has bolted, wouldn't you say?' he answered. 'I know Rosalind very well and, as well as having some very lovable traits, she can at times be quite cold and calculating. She won't give up easily, so now she's seen you here, nothing is going to change by your leaving.'

'If you're sure?' Bevin murmured hesitantly, knowing that having lost her own inheritance, her home no longer home with Irene ruling the roost, she did not want to leave Jarvis's apartment—not just yet.

'I'm sure,' he stated, and gave her an encouraging smile before going on lightly, 'Though, with you in evidence, I reckon they must be planning a backing-off campaign to see if they have more success that way.'

'Backing-off campaign?' she echoed.

'I expected my father to have phoned before this,' he explained. 'The fact that he hasn't can only mean that they've had their heads together.'

He made it sound like war! Though to him, since he valued his freedom so much, it probably felt that way, Bevin realised. 'Your sister will have been in touch with your parents?' she questioned.

'Apart from her frequent sessions on the phone with my mother, she lives only about ten miles from the Manor.'

'Manor?' she queried.

'The family pile,' he replied lightly, and Bevin realised she had been right to believe that his grandfather had left quite some considerable amount—plus. By the sound of it, Jarvis came from a wealthy background.

But this wasn't helping him in any way, and after his goodness to her she wanted to do what she could to help. 'If you gave me your sister's number, I could ring her and explain that you were only being good to me when . . .' She broke off when Jarvis shook his head.

'I told her over the phone yesterday that you and I were just good friends,' he revealed.

'But she didn't believe you?'

'She reminded me, in case I'd forgotten, that you'd been wearing the pyjamas she'd given me as a Christmas present.'

Bevin began to feel pink about the cheeks at the obvious connotation his sister must have put on the fact that she was wearing Jarvis's pyjamas, and hurried on to protest, 'But didn't you explain about me being unwell—about you looking after me?'

'Of course,' he confirmed matter-of-factly—and shrugged. 'It was an exercise in digging my own grave. Rosalind, who has conveniently forgotten the hours I spent with our grandfather at the end, has memory from way back apparently of how I could never bear to be near a sickroom. According to her, and nothing's going to shake her view, to not only have lent my pyjamas to someone who's ill, but to have them stay in my bachelor apartment too, *must* mean that I'm in love.'

What could she say? For his very kindness, it seemed, he was damned. 'I'm sorry,' she said sincerely, and feeling she carried a lot of the blame, 'Is there anything I can do? Nothing you can do?'

'Not while Rosalind has this particular bee in her bonnet. And nothing I can do while the family badger me to marry but sit it out and wait for my thirty-seventh birthday to pass.'

'Isn't there anyone among the women you know whom you—er—fancy enough to marry?' she enquired tentatively.

'Fancy enough to give up my freedom?' he asked, astounded, the idea clearly not filling him with enthusiasm. 'I should have to like someone particularly well before...' Suddenly he stopped dead. Then, his look thoughtful, to her utter astonishment, he stated offhandedly, 'I could marry you, I suppose.'

Bevin managed to cope with her astonishment, but not with the anger that quickly followed it. She could do without his offhanded and never-meant-to-be-taken-seriously proposals, thank you very much, and she wasted no time in telling him so.

'Don't do me any favours!' she snapped suddenly, the temper which had only surfaced since she had known him rising again as, her eyes flashing, she sprang up from the table.

Though if she was astonished by what he had said, he appeared incredulous at what she had replied. His eyes on her sparking brown ones, he rose too and, to her mind making it seem that he'd got women queuing up to marry him, 'You mean—you're actually turning down my proposal?' he asked disbelievingly.

'Got it in one!' she snapped. The nerve of him! If he *was* serious—and she was sure he wasn't—then he was as cold and as calculating as he'd stated his sister could be.

For long moments, while she glared at him, Jarvis just stood and surveyed her. Then she thought she saw a sudden glint come to his eyes, and had a peculiar feeling that, by turning him down, she had just become something of a challenge to him.

She knew almost immediately that she was mistaken in that idea, however, and that she represented no challenge whatsoever when he agreed, his tone easy, even a hint of a smile on his mouth, 'Perhaps you're right. Maybe it wasn't one of my better ideas.' And, closing the subject firmly shut, 'You look as if you're out on your feet,' he decided. 'Why not go to bed— I'll clear up here.'

At any other time, Bevin might have insisted on staying to lend a hand with the clearing up. But she owned to feeling shaken—as much by his proposal as her reaction to it. She had no idea why she had flown into such a passion over it, but suddenly she felt a very strong need to be by herself. So she bade him 'Goodnight,' and left him to it.

CHAPTER FIVE

BEVIN stirred in her sleep, and opened her eyes to see Jarvis, having just deposited a cup of tea on her bedside table, turning as if to tiptoe out.

'What time is it?' she mumbled dreamily.

'Go back to sleep,' Jarvis instructed in gentle, quiet tones—and Bevin came more awake to remember the shopping list she had written down when she had left him last night.

'Don't forget the groceries,' she told him drowsily, and roused still further to note that the shopping list was no longer on the bedside table.

'Yes, dear,' he said obediently, and suddenly, at the hint of amusement in his tones, Bevin woke up—and suddenly, as she looked across at him, they both burst out laughing. Then, 'See you,' Jarvis nodded, and, clearly wanting an early start to the day, he went swiftly from the room.

Without meaning to, Bevin did go back to sleep after he'd gone, and awoke about an hour later feeling very much better than she had been feeling, but even so, not feeling very much like rushing around.

She had a bath and changed into fresh pyjamas, then, taking the white and fluffy towels from the bathroom and any other bits of laundry, she went and started the washing machine, then set about tidying around. She felt she would like to have collected any laundry in Jarvis's bathroom and put that to wash too, but she realised it must be enough of an intrusion on him having her to stay anyway. Most certainly he would object if, even just wanting to do something for him for a change, she went through the private area of his bedroom to his bathroom.

Which thought, that she must be enough of an intrusion, made her think seriously about returning to Abbot's Cheney. She made herself a cup of coffee. She'd leave it until tomorrow, she mused, and, happily remembering how Jarvis had complimented her on last night's meal and how he'd as good as asked her to cook a meal for him that night, she didn't see how she could possibly return to her own home before then.

Later, when the laundry had been tumble-dried, Bevin rescued her underwear and shirt, then went and got dressed. A short while after that, the doorbell rang. Her first, panicking thought was that the caller was Rosalind, Jarvis's sister. But while she was seriously contemplating not answering the door rather than give his sister more fuel for the fire, she almost simultaneously recalled how Jarvis had thought his family might now be adopting a 'backing-off campaign'—and also remembered that Jarvis was going to have some groceries sent in.

The bell pealed again and, suddenly fearful that the van driver would take the goods away again if he thought no one was in, she flew to the door.

'Thought you were out,' a wiry man, looking weighed down by an enormous box filled to the top, greeted her. 'Where do you want these, madam?'

. 'Er—in the kitchen,' she smiled, and led the way.

No sooner had the man gone than Bevin started work unloading the box. She enjoyed filling up Jarvis's fridge and cupboards, and was glad she'd ordered enough flour and fillings to be able to stock his

freezer up. The time was getting on now for her to
start, but she'd have a baking session before she left
tomorrow, she decided, and began making prep-
arations for that evening's meal.

When Jarvis came home that night there was again
a delicious aroma coming from the kitchen. 'I could
get to enjoy this,' he greeted Bevin, coming straight
to where she was in the kitchen, briefcase and all.
'What are we having tonight?' he asked, sniffing
appreciatively.

'A fish starter, followed by chicken Kiev, a few veg-
etables and a side salad, with apple pie to follow—
any good?'

'Do I have to wait until eight o'clock?' he responded, and while she was aware that he was joking,
Bevin felt good inside.

That good feeling stayed around when later they
sat together in his dining-room and chatted the
mealtime away. Jarvis had asked her if she was allowed alcohol with the medicines she was taking, and
had decreed, since an inspection of the labels made
no mention of any such prohibition, that one glass
wouldn't hurt her.

'This is a superb wine,' she remarked after a sip of
a beautiful-tasting Gewürztraminer.

'This,' Jarvis told her, 'is a superb meal.'

'Your chicken's all right?'

'Excellent,' he replied. 'In fact, I'd go as far as to
say this must rate as the second-best meal I've had in
a year.'

She laughed, she couldn't help it. 'I love it when
you lie,' she told him, and realised that, for the first
time in an age, she felt happy. Her laughter faded,
though, when she saw his glance go from her eyes to

her parted smiling mouth and, his expression suddenly serious, back up to her eyes again. 'Is something wrong?' she asked.

'Not a thing,' he said at once. 'I was just wondering, though, if after a meal such as this you can be so heartless as to expect me to bring home a takeaway tomorrow night.'

'I . . .' she began, and, happy with him in his home, she knew she didn't want to leave. Not just yet—when she knew in advance that in the home she would soon have to go to, she would be anything but happy. 'Are you saying you'd like me to cook a meal for you tomorrow night too?' she asked.

'Why not stay on here until you're really fit?' he suggested. And, making her feel she had in no way overstayed her welcome, 'Stay until Sunday, anyhow,' he suggested, then smiled as he added, 'and I'll drop you to your home after we've eaten the delectable Sunday roast you're going to make for me.'

'What can a girl say?' she laughed, though, as the thought struck her, she asked, 'You're—er—not entertaining this weekend?' and saw that he had at once caught her drift.

'I'm keeping a low profile on entertaining for the next five months,' he told her. 'And for certain, I shan't be "entertaining at home" until after then.'

At home, where his sister or parents might unexpectedly call, Bevin realised, and realised that Jarvis obviously felt safe with her. She didn't know how she felt about that. Though his family knew about her anyway and—she brightened—Jarvis, even though he had not meant it, had asked her to marry him.

As on the previous evening Jarvis said he would
clear everything up after the meal. 'I'll help,' she
volunteered at once.

'No, you won't,' he told her firmly. 'You're not as
well as you think you are yet,' he added in a tone
there was no arguing with.

'I'll bet you can be a real tough nut sometimes,'
she opined, giving in.

'Only when I have to be,' he grinned.

'Enjoy the washing-up,' she told him, and with his
grin suddenly doing fluttery things to her insides, she
decided to go to bed. 'Goodnight,' she smiled, and
left him.

The next time she saw him was the next morning
when, business-suited, he went quietly out of her room
after leaving a cup of tea for her on her bedside table.
She opened her mouth to call out a greeting, but
inexplicably then she discovered she was suddenly
beset by a feeling of shyness, and by the time she had
got herself back together and to wonder what on earth
had brought that on, Jarvis was gone.

She did not linger in bed that morning, but, at the
thought that Jarvis, through a goodness in his
nature—despite a hint she had seen last night that he
could be tough when the occasion demanded it—had
invited her to prolong her stay until Sunday, she got
out of bed. She had some baking to do.

Once she was bathed and dressed, she went along
to the kitchen and set about first sealing some chunks
of steak and kidney before setting it to cook through
for a couple of hours. She was starting to work on
the filling for some chicken and mushroom pies when
she again thought of Jarvis's toughness. Her mind
went back to how he'd gone straight for her jugular

on Monday when he'd come home and wanted to know why she hadn't told him his sister had called at his apartment the day before. His fury, like his charm, was a potent force.

Pleasant thoughts of Jarvis popped into her head on and off throughout that morning. As well as making some steak and kidney pies for the freezer, she would make steak and kidney for dinner tonight, followed by a fresh fruit salad, she thought, and having completed all the fillings, she had a brief rest for lunch, then set to work on making some pastry. Then the door bell rang.

For one or two startled moments, Bevin again thought it was Jarvis's sister Rosalind at the door. But as the ring at the door came again—much as it had yesterday—she told herself not to be silly, that she'd got his sister on her brain, and she quickly rinsed her hands and went to answer. Quite obviously, she thought, a smile coming to her face, Jarvis had decided—since until Sunday she was still chief cook— to have some more groceries delivered.

Anticipating that it would be the same little man to whom she'd opened the door yesterday, Bevin was still smiling as she pulled the door back. But it was not the same little man but an elegant and expensively turned out woman who stood there, a fair-haired woman of about thirty, and Bevin's smile started to slip.

'You're still here, then,' the woman remarked, quite pleasantly.

'Jarvis has . . . I . . .' Bevin tried, but feeling suddenly helpless as the other woman stepped over the threshold and sniffed the air, she could only be glad she was wearing her own clothes and not the pyjamas this woman had selected. 'I've been doing a spot of cooking,' she explained the cooking smells, and could have groaned aloud at how stupid that sounded.

'So I see—you've got flour on your cheek,' Jarvis Devilliers' sister commented. And, giving Bevin a sharp, direct look, 'When are you going to make it legal?' she questioned.

'Make what...?' Bevin began to ask, then discovered that Jarvis wasn't the only member of his family who could get tough when the occasion called for it, for abruptly his sister was cutting her off.

'Oh, come on!' she exclaimed impatiently. And, when Bevin just wasn't ready for her attitude or the question, 'Jarvis *has* asked you to marry him, hasn't he?'

'Yes—but...'

'But just for the hell of it he's asked you to wait until after June before...'

'*No!*' Bevin protested sharply. Honestly, this woman—she wasn't letting her get a word in edgeways to tell her the truth of the matter!

Nor was she, because before Bevin could draw breath to explain, she exclaimed joyously, 'You're getting married *before* my brother's birthday!' and suddenly looking as though all her dreams had just come true, she went steamrollering on, 'I'm Rosalind, by the way. I'm...'

This had gone far enough. 'I know,' said Bevin, and went on quickly, 'but you should know...'

'He's told you about me!' Rosalind smiled, and was deaf, it seemed, to anything but that which she wanted to hear as, turning back to the door, she announced, 'We'll be great friends, I'm sure.' She opened the door. 'Can't stop now, though. Masses to do.'

'But...' Bevin attempted, and even followed her out of the flat. 'Rosalind!' she called. 'I ... It ...' But Rosalind was getting into the lift, and as the door of Jarvis's flat began to close to, Bevin's first priority, having left some stock simmering on the stove, was to prevent herself being locked out of the flat.

She made it quite comfortably, but closing the door behind her she went and sat on a chair in the kitchen feeling absolutely poleaxed. It had all been so fast! She just wasn't used to dealing with hard-nosed straight-to-the-point people like the Rosalinds of this world. But what had she done now! Only as good as let Jarvis's sister go away with the impression that she and Jarvis would be getting married before he was thirty-seven. Jarvis would kill her!

A moment later Bevin was getting up from her chair, knowing that whatever else she didn't know, she couldn't sit there all afternoon doing nothing. She glanced at her watch. It was about two minutes past two. Should she ring him, or should she just find her scarf and coat and quietly leave?

Of course she must ring him, she recognised a second later, if only to warn him, if only to clear herself. Without a doubt his sister would be ringing him the first chance she got—*and* his parents, she realised. Oh lord!.

A minute later she had left the kitchen, and her half-made pastry, and was hunting for the phone book. She guessed she might not so easily be able to speak to Jarvis, though she thought that if she left her name and asked him to ring her back most urgently, Jarvis might ring her at his first opportunity.

'Can I speak to Mr Devilliers?' she asked as soon as she got through to the Devilliers' head office.

'Can you tell me what it's in connection with?' her request was pleasantly countered.

'This is a personal call,' Bevin replied pleasantly.

'Just a moment.'

The next she knew, another female voice was asking if she could help her. 'I wanted to speak with Mr Devilliers on a personal matter,' Bevin explained.

'I'm sorry, he's at a meeting which started five minutes ago,' she was genially put off.

'Can I speak with Mr Devilliers' secretary?' asked Bevin with a persistence born of panic.

'I'm afraid Dawn Lewis, Mr Devilliers' PA, is in the meeting with him,' the girl told her, but volunteered, 'I'm Amanda Restall, Dawn's assistant—can I help in any way?'

'I wonder if you can give him a message as soon as the meeting is over?' asked Bevin.

'I'm afraid I won't be seeing either Dawn or Mr Devilliers again today,' Amanda Restall told her. 'The meeting Mr Devilliers is chairing is scheduled to last some hours. Mr Devilliers particularly requested no interruptions, so I'm unable to get a message through. Not, of course,' she qualified, 'unless it's an extremely "life or death" kind of message.'

For a moment or two Bevin gave full consideration to saying that her message was that urgent. But, 'No, it's not that urgent,' she sighed—Jarvis would just love it, wouldn't he, if in the middle of what sounded like some high-powered business meeting someone broke into his important agenda with a message to ring her. 'Thank you anyway,' she told Amanda Restall, and rang off.

A minute later Bevin was deeply involved with what
course of action she should take now, when it suddenly dawned on her that if she couldn't get through
to speak to Jarvis on the phone, then neither could
his sister! All at once she felt as though a ton weight
had been lifted off her, and she returned to the
kitchen.

She could not have said she was anywhere near as
happy as she had been, though. For the mere fact that
Rosalind would not be able to phone her brother as
she had that last time did not make the problem go
away. But, as Bevin gave her attention to pastry, pies
and fruit salad, at least she was going to have the
chance to tell Jarvis what had occurred in advance
and give him a chance to decide how best to cope with
it.

That it was certain she was going to have to confess
everything to Jarvis when he came home was patently
clear, but since he must know his sister well, Bevin
hoped he would understand how such a thing could
have occurred.

Over the following hours, though, the subject refused to leave her mind, so that as the time arrived
when Jarvis had come home on the three previous
nights, she had started to worry on another front. She
had been grateful to realise that Rosalind wouldn't be
speaking to Jarvis before she did, but what was there
to prevent Rosalind from ringing her parents with the
'glad news'?

Bevin had the meal she had prepared all ready for
finishing off when she heard Jarvis's key in the lock,
and, anticipating that if his meeting had been so
lengthy, then it could well have been problematical,
she seriously toyed with the idea of letting him eat

first before she gave him another problem to deal with.
But was that being cowardly or considerate? She
couldn't decide which.

The sudden thought, though, that since his sister
would know his phone number and might, in the
frustration of being unable to get him at his office,
ring him at his home, at any minute, or worse, call
in person, and might even now be on her way to his
door, caused Bevin to hurry from the kitchen.

She met Jarvis in the sitting-room, where it looked
as if he had been striding to find her. He halted abruptly when he saw her, however, as she did the
moment she saw his thunderous expression. She saw
him toss his briefcase in the direction of a couch, and
there was something in his action, his look, that
warned he wasn't very pleased about something. Oh
grief, she thought, having heard hair-raising tales from
her father about stormy board meetings—and here
she was about to add to Jarvis's troubles!

'You don't look as though your day has gone particularly well,' she began, sensitively feeling her way—
and had that question promptly ignored for her
efforts.

Because, his look growing more and more hostile
by the minute, he made no answer about how his day
had gone, but his chin thrust aggressively forward as
he snarled, 'You've picked out a ring, of course!'

'Ring?' she questioned, her mind a blank as to what
he could be meaning for all of a second. Then, as a
sick feeling hit the pit of her stomach, light began to
dawn. 'Oh no!' she exclaimed. 'Your sister *did* phone
you!'

'Oh no,' he mocked harshly, 'she didn't!'

'But...'

'She did better than *that*!' he grated. And, causing Bevin to stare at him in wide-eyed amazement, 'She drove down to London, to my office.'

'But...' Bevin began, her thoughts scattered.

'And before anyone could stop her,' he forged straight on as though she hadn't spoken, 'she charged into an important meeting I was chairing, because she was "so thrilled",' he mimicked, 'she couldn't wait to "*congratulate*" me on my engagement!'

'No!' gasped Bevin, her thoughts still scattered. 'Oh *no*!' she protested. She strove to gather together what wits she could. 'You denied it, of course!' she said in a hoarse whisper.

'I should deny "I'm so happy for you! I can't tell you how overjoyed I was when Bevin told me you'd asked her to marry you"?' he gritted explosively.

'I never... I did—but I didn't... It wasn't like that!' Bevin stammered, then started to get angry herself. '*Dammit*!' she suddenly erupted. 'I couldn't get a word in. She just carried on regardless! Bamboozling me to say things I didn't mean to say—pushing me into a corner. She's just like you. There's...' At the unyielding expression on his face, Bevin suddenly knew he just wasn't prepared to see her side of it, and abruptly she broke off to go storming past him.

'So now it's my fault!' he barked, as she reached the door into the hall. 'My fault that the Press have got hold of it!'

Bevin took one step further and all her senses suddenly started screaming in horror. She stopped dead in her tracks and turned slowly round. 'Oh—no!' she whispered shakenly.

'Oh yes!' he retorted toughly. But all at once he was rocking back on his heels, and a mocking light had suddenly entered his eyes. 'Going to give your fiancé a kiss?' he drawled.

Bevin was still staring shakenly at him. But, at his mockery, at the mocking way he alluded to her as being betrothed to him, so more spirit came to her aid. 'Get lost!' she yelled at him, and marched into the hall and along to her room.

Once there, though, it was as though all the stuffing suddenly went out of her. Her legs felt weak, she felt weak, and, as she sank down to sit on the edge of her bed, she began to bitterly blame herself.

She'd tried to blame Rosalind, then, when Jarvis was blameless, tried to put some of the blame on him. But in reality it was all her fault. She'd known the score. She'd known that his sister was anxious for him to marry before the next five months were out. She'd known that his parents were just as anxious too. She should have been on her guard from the moment she'd answered the door and seen Rosalind there, she realised dejectedly.

That she hadn't been on her guard stemmed from the rather non-eventful life she led, she thought dismally. Though almost at once she corrected herself. Life *had* been uneventful—and then her father had died, and it somehow seemed impossible that so much had happened since then. First Irene had waltzed in, scented money—and stayed. Then Oliver Taylor, who so far as she could remember had until then never so much as held her hand, had, to her amazement, asked her to marry him. Then, if that wasn't enough to have happened in such a short space, flu brought on by shock, so she gathered, had seen her entrusting herself to a complete stranger, living in his home and, she owned, liking it.

But none of that was any help with the problem that, by just being in Jarvis's apartment, she had created. She felt defeated as she realised that he had every right to be furious, then she heard a small sound in the room, and looked up to see that Jarvis had followed her and had come to stand in her bedroom doorway.

He didn't look furious any more, she noted. That mocking light had gone from his eyes too, she observed, leaving him stern-looking and not overjoyed with the world at present.

She took her glance from him, and stared dispiritedly down at her feet. She heard him move and felt the mattress give as he came and sat beside her on the bed.

She owed him an apology, and she knew it, but she felt so dejected then that it was an effort to speak. 'It's all down to me, isn't it?' she said quietly. 'I was steamrollered, but you'd told me Rosalind could be cold and calculating. Not, though, about her hard-nosed, get-to-the-point tactics—but I suppose I should have been ready for it.'

'How did it happen?' he asked quietly, seeming more reasonable now than he had been.

'Even now I'm not sure,' Bevin confessed. 'I answered the door, Rosalind stood there, then she came in, and before I knew it she was impatiently demanding if you'd asked me to marry you. I found I'd said "yes" before I could think. Then, while I was still trying to qualify that, she was on her way out, and I discovered I'd given her the impression—don't ask me how—that you and I are getting married before your next birthday. I didn't mean to, I swear I didn't,' Bevin ended miserably, and turning to look at him, she went on, 'I tried straight away to get you at your office, but Amanda Restall, your PA's assistant, said you were in some lengthy meeting and that she wouldn't see you again that day, so I saw no point in leaving a message. I thought,' she added lamely, 'that if I couldn't get to speak to you on the phone, then Rosalind couldn't either.' Her warm brown eyes were large and unhappy as she asked, 'You do believe me?'

'Of course,' he said quietly, and Bevin realised then that, had there been any doubt in his mind, she wouldn't be sitting where she was now. In fact, she probably wouldn't even be sitting in his flat. Though he'd got a clear right to be upset about it, she accepted—then thought she'd better get it all over with now.

'Your sister will have been in touch with your parents by this time, won't she?' she realised. There was no hiding from that fact.

'It had to be Rosalind or my father who tipped off the Press,' Jarvis agreed.

'Oh, lord!' She'd forgotten that for a moment. But she accepted that, without question, the doings of the head of a company as big as Devilliers were bound to be of interest to the press. 'What are we going to do?' she asked deflatedly.

Jarvis shrugged. 'Get engaged for a while?' he suggested, but already Bevin was shaking her head.

'That wouldn't be fair to you, or your family,' she said, and suddenly started to tingle all over when, his look softening, he placed an arm lightly across her shoulders.

'You're worried about my family after the way Rosalind bulldozed you?' he asked, but, not waiting for an answer, 'And what's fair to you, little Bevin?'

he questioned, and went on, 'You with your alive intelligence, who've been too busy looking after your father to have a chance to go in for a career should you have so wished.'

'I was going to do accountancy,' she confessed, even while she felt flattered by his compliment, feeling shaken that he had bothered to think beyond the sketchy outline she had given him of her life. 'But I loved my father,' she added hastily, lest Jarvis thought she had stayed home grudgingly to take care of him.

'And got well repaid for it by him, didn't you?' Jarvis commented bluntly.

'I think you're missing the point,' Bevin told him. 'Love doesn't expect payment.'

'Which is just as well, since, through your father's neglect, some shark of a woman has come in and claimed what's rightfully yours.'

'She's spoiled it all anyhow, now,' she said gently. But suddenly she stilled, for all at once Jarvis was looking at her in a very tender way.

'I think, Bevin Pemberton,' he said quietly, 'that you must be one of the nicest women I have ever met.' And, so saying, he leant forward and gently touched his lips to hers.

'Oh!' she breathed, and owned, as her heart hastened its beat, that she rather liked the feel of his superb, warm and gentle mouth against hers.

She rather gathered then that Jarvis wasn't averse to the touch of her lips beneath his either, for her mouth was still in its 'oh' shape when he leant forward, and touched his mouth to hers again. Then, as round-eyed she looked at him, he pulled back, but when she made no move to pull out of his arm, suddenly that arm tightened about her shoulders. Sud-

denly his other arm was round her too, and suddenly
Jarvis was kissing her again.

How her arms came to be up around him as she
clung on tightly to him, Bevin never knew. She had
no memory of moving her arms, but used them to
cling on to him as he parted her lips with his, and
kissed her again and again, drawing the very soul from
her.

'Oh, Jarvis!' she breathed shakily when she suddenly discovered that she was no longer sitting on the
side of her bed with him, but with her shoes kicked
off, his shoes kicked off, his jacket gone, she was lying
on the bed with him. His kisses were something en-
tirely outside her experience!

Nor were his kisses confined to her mouth, for, to
light yet more fire in her, he traced expert kisses down
the side of her throat, down to the V of her shirt, and
when her buttons restricted him, he had the answer
for that too.

His mouth returned to hers while gently, unhurriedly, his long sensitive fingers undid the buttons of
her shirt. Then once more he bent his head to her
breast and kissed the valley in between, and Bevin
awakened to the new experience of wanting a man—
not just any man, but Jarvis.

She wasn't sure she didn't call out his name when
his hands caressed to her breasts and he captured
them. Though when she pressed her body against him
the nearer to get to him, she heard an anguished groan
of wanting escape him. Passion such as she had never
known stormed through her then. She wanted him,
and only him.

Suddenly, though, as Jarvis undid the waistband of
her trousers and caressed with warm hands over the

flatness of her belly, Bevin was taken by an over-
whelming shyness. A shyness which until then had
been conspicuous by its absence. 'I can't!' she gasped
suddenly, and in sudden panic she pushed his hands
from her and, like someone suddenly demented, shot
into a sitting position.

'You *can't!*' Jarvis exploded gruffly, and Bevin,
having given him all the signs, she knew, that she
'*could*', did not blame him at all when, his aggression
suddenly out in full force, he demanded, 'Why the
hell not?'

'I'm sorry,' she nearly fell over herself to apologise.
'I know I've—er—led you on, I think, but I c-can't,'
she repeated, hardly knowing what she was saying,
'b-because—I never have.'

She knew that was a lame excuse, and nothing of
an answer. But she hoped he wouldn't press her,
though she felt so shaken emotionally that she wasn't
sure about that either. Though she wasn't in any doubt
that she wanted his arms about her again.

'You never have?' Jarvis was questioning toughly,
as though he did not understand what on earth she
was talking about. Then in the next instant she realised
that he'd made the connection, for all at once the
tough note had gone from his voice. 'You never
have—you're a virgin, Bevin?' he asked, but he
seemed—when in the heat of the moment he had forgotten—to have already suspected that fact. For then
he was taking what sounded like a much-needed
steadying breath.

But while Bevin nodded, she was desperately
striving to get off the subject, to cool it, to try to
remember what they'd been talking about before
Jarvis had kissed her.

'Any-anyway,' she took up, her voice shaky as, feeling very much in need of a steadying breath herself, she buttoned up her shirt and attempted to go on as though nothing had happened, 'we—er—can't pretend to be engaged.'

Jarvis, seeming to accept her 'I can't' without further question, must be using mammoth efforts to gain some self-control as well, she realised. He had moved to sit up too, anyhow. 'Why not?' he asked.

'B-because your family will be furious when we break the engagement,' she explained, striving with all she had to keep her feet back down on the ground after the most earth-rocking experience of her life.

Her task wasn't made any easier, though, when all at once Jarvis placed a hand under her chin and turned her round to face him. 'We—needn't break it. We needn't pretend,' he said, and everything went haywire in Bevin.

She stared at him, her lovely brown eyes saucer-wide. There was a warm look in his eyes for her, she saw, and her heart beat crazily away inside her. Then abruptly she asked herself, how else would he look at her but warmly? For heaven's sake, hadn't they, barely minutes ago, been in the middle of some very heated lovemaking?

From somewhere and with her heart beating so furiously away inside her, she knew not where, Bevin found a matter-of-fact note as she told him, 'Oh, you're just being—er—passionate.'

For one stunned moment Jarvis looked at her, and then, causing her to be heartily glad she hadn't taken him seriously, all at once he burst out laughing. Then, as his laughter faded, he commented drily, 'You're not without passion yourself.'

'Oh—that's you!' she freely blamed him.

'My fault again?' he asked, his right eyebrow twitching upwards, and Bevin felt the pink in her cheeks from his lovemaking deepen.

'Nobody's ever...' she tried to explain. 'I didn't know I could feel...' she broke off helplessly, and loved Jarvis as much as she liked him when he came in to help her out.

'Confused you, have I?' he enquired gently.

'A bit,' she understated, and, needing suddenly then more than at any time in her life to be alone, she was grateful to him again when he stood up, slipped his shoes back on and, picking up his jacket, strolled casually towards the door.

And she loved him even more when he asked, as if seeking to help her by changing the subject, 'What's for dinner?'

'Steak and kidney,' she told him, and knew as he closed the door behind him that it was true: she did love him. Was, in fact, very much in love with him—it had been growing and growing within her from the very first moment he had spoken to her!

CHAPTER SIX

SEATED on the side of her bed where Jarvis had left her, Bevin faced the fact of her love for him. She would have liked to believe that her feelings for him were a figment of her imagination brought on by him awakening senses which she had never known she possessed. But it wasn't that. She was in love with him. The certain knowledge was there—and it wouldn't go away.

This, then, she suddenly realised, was why she had been so passionate in her refusal of his offhand marriage proposal on Tuesday. Even then her subconscious must have been aware of her love and the fact that she didn't want any offhand proposal—she wanted a serious one.

Bevin got up from the bed knowing, when she would have preferred not to see Jarvis again that night, that she had dinner to attend to. She went to the bathroom to rinse her hands and to tidy herself up, but was glad to see from the mirror that she didn't look any different now that she had recognised her love for Jarvis than she had before. Good, she thought on a shaky breath, if she couldn't see any sign, then neither would he—he must never know how she felt about him.

She took another shaky breath before she left her room, but made it to the kitchen without seeing Jarvis. She could hear him moving around, though, and had just put some potatoes on to boil when, his damp-darkened hair showing he had recently showered, he sauntered into the kitchen.

Bevin felt her cheeks go a warm pink from the memory of how when they had last been together she had clung on tightly to him. Clung on and, without a thought of protest, allowed his hands to explore the upper part of her body. But, if he was remembering such detail, or if he had noticed her sudden rush of colour, he gave no indication but, his voice even, neither warm nor cold, but just plain matter-of-fact, he enquired, 'How long will dinner be?'

'Half an hour,' she replied, proud of the matter-of-fact tone she had managed to pull off herself. 'I'll give you a shout if you want to do half an hour's work before then,' she volunteered.

'Have a heart!' he protested, as if calling her a slavedriver. 'I was thinking more in terms of laying the table.'

'It's done,' she told him, but was relieved when he left the kitchen just the same, and thanked her lucky stars that he had not seen how inwardly she was shaken, just to have him standing so near.

Dinner was a quieter meal than on previous occasions, for where before they had conversed freely on all subjects, Jarvis that evening seemed rather preoccupied. And she, Bevin accepted, wasn't feeling in a very talkative mood either. Perhaps she would adjust to the startling knowledge that had made itself known to her when she had been in his arms, but for the moment she was still feeling stunned.

She did not feel very hungry, but ate all she had placed on her plate, and was afterwards helping Jarvis to some fruit salad, when he suddenly stated, 'We can't pretend this "engagement" never happened, Bevin.'

'No, I suppose not,' she replied, aware that Jarvis was not the kind of a man who would hope that, if they did nothing, the problem might go away. Quite obviously he'd decided that they were going to have to talk about it.

'As I see it, there are several options we can take,' he went on, and Bevin realised he must have been giving the matter some thought now that his fury about his sister breaking into his meeting to congratulate him on his engagement had subsided. 'We could,' he deliberated, 'or rather I could, make it work to my advantage.'

'Oh?' she enquired carefully, and listened intently as Jarvis, having addressed the problem, outlined his findings.

'It's clear that any backing-off campaign I'd imagined my family were now adopting, hasn't lasted long. It's clear, too, that should I deny to the Press that I'm engaged to be married, my family are going to pile on the pressure with renewed vigour.'

'Oh, grief!' Bevin exclaimed unhappily.

'Double grief is what I'd term it,' he responded gravely.

'You mean—you won't have only your sister charging into serious business meetings you're chairing, but your father too?'

'I said you were intelligent,' he commented, to denote she'd about got it right. 'Though you haven't mentioned the visits to my apartment door, the phone calls, the emotional blackmail, the...'

'Don't go on!' She couldn't bear it. And she sighed, as she demonstrated the intelligence he had dubbed

her with. 'Are you saying you want us to pretend to
be engaged for a little while?'

'It would keep my family off my neck at a time
when I just don't need outside distractions,' he replied, and made her feel good inside that he trusted
her when he went on to confide, 'I'm heavily involved
right now in discussions with finance people and
another engineering company about the prospect of
going for a take-over.'

'Oh, Jarvis,' Bevin mumbled, her good feeling re-
placed by worry. She wanted to help, couldn't bear
that he should be under such pressure from not only
his business life, but in his private life too, but she
could not say she felt very happy about being party
to deceiving his family. 'How long would it be for—
the pretend engagement, I mean?' she asked.

He shrugged, but answered honestly, 'Would five
months be too long?'

'Couldn't you—er—hint to your family before
then?'

'I could,' he agreed, 'but even though they don't
need Grandfather's money, they'd again be beating a
path to both this apartment door and my office door
if I did.'

'They're going to do that again anyway when you
don't show any signs of getting married within those
five months,' Bevin pointed out.

'True,' he conceded, and thought for a moment,
then suggested, 'How do you feel about us being "engaged" for as long as it takes for me to get something
achieved in this take-over?'

Bevin had no idea how long take-overs took, or
indeed for how long this particular take-over had been
on the boil. But, as she supposed she'd known since

the moment that she'd acknowledged her love for him, that love meant she would go along with pretty much anything he said.

So she agreed quietly, undramatically, 'Until then, then.'

'Thank you, Bevin,' he said, and seeming much relieved, 'For that, I'll do the washing-up.'

'That's my department,' she countered. 'You go and do what take-over merchants do studywise.'

'Ye gods, the man who finally gets you will have to watch his step!' Jarvis grumbled good-naturedly at her bossing him around—and Bevin laughed.

Jarvis had looked less stern than he had, she thought as he went in the direction of his study and she went kitchenwards. But, even if it was a foregone conclusion that the man who finally got her would not, sadly, be Jarvis, the tension that had been building up in her since before dinner was all at once broken.

She did not see him again that night, but completed the dish-washing. Then, as the pies she'd made that day were now cold and ready for the freezer, she labelled them and put them away, and went to her room.

Since she had gone to sleep with Jarvis in her head, it was no surprise to her that he was in her head again before she opened her eyes on Friday morning. Had she only known him for a week? It seemed incredible. Yet how long did it take to fall in love? There *was* no set time.

She opened her eyes and saw that it was daylight outside and that she had slept later than usual. She glanced at her bedside table, half expecting to see a cup of tea sitting there, but there was no cup and saucer. She wondered if Jarvis had overslept and listened for sounds of him moving around, but could hear none.

Pushing back the covers, she grabbed at the towelling robe at the bottom of the bed and was struggling into it as she went. Since she had no idea how late Jarvis had worked last night, it was in her mind to go hammering on his door to wake him. For no known reason, though, she went in the direction of the kitchen first, and it was there that she discovered that Jarvis was already up and about and, since there was no sign or sound of him, must have left for his office. The teapot was cold, but the coffee-pot was warm. He'd rinsed the cup and saucer, and the plate he'd used, she saw, but had left them there to dry.

Bevin went slowly back to her room, feeling glad she was there. She turned her thoughts away from such treacherous yearnings as to want to be there permanently, and contented herself that at least, after a tough day, Jarvis wouldn't have to fend for himself in the kitchen that night.

She went and had her bath, but was in the middle of deciding whether to have something rice- or pasta-based for a main course that night, when she was suddenly electrified into action when the fact that it was a Friday started to have some significance. Wasn't Friday the day Jarvis's cleaning lady, Mrs Underhill, was due?

A few minutes later Bevin was out of her bath and speedily getting dressed. She didn't know if Jarvis had been in touch with Mrs Underhill to tell her that he had a guest, but she didn't want to be caught wearing next to nothing when she arrived.

Bevin next busied herself tidying round her room. She had no idea what time Mrs Underhill usually came, but when at nine-thirty the doorbell sounded, she knew it must be her.

As she went to answer the door she surmised that Jarvis must have phoned his cleaning lady to tell her he had a guest. How thoughtful of the woman not to use her key, Bevin mused. Had she not remembered Mrs Underhill in time—had Mrs Underhill used her key—she'd have jumped out of her skin to hear someone entering the apartment at this time of day.

Bevin had her fingers on the door catch and was just about to turn it when suddenly she halted. All at once it occurred to her that maybe it wasn't Mrs Underhill on the other side! The bell sounded again, reminding her that she couldn't stand there all day making up her mind what to do.

She thought of Jarvis and how, for his sake, she was 'engaged' to him. It was then that she decided she was going to take her time in answering his sister's pertinent questions and that, if it was Rosalind on the other side of the door, she just was not going to be steamrollered into giving the wrong answers today. She turned the latch and pulled back the door—and got yet another nasty shock!

Bevin had never seen Mrs Underhill before, but she saw at once that it wasn't her. Nor was it Jarvis's sister Rosalind who stood there. But—and Bevin could hardly believe her eyes—the woman who stood there, and seemed about to press the doorbell for the third time, was none other than Irene, her stepmother.

'I knew I'd find you here!' Irene boomed triumphantly.

'You've been looking for me?' Bevin questioned, not trusting Irene's smiling look for a second, but at a complete loss to know what she was doing there.

'I've been concerned about you, naturally,' Irene answered, causing Bevin to stare at her in complete amazement.

'You've been concerned—about *me*?' she just had to question that statement—on the evidence she had seen so far the only person Irene was concerned about was Irene Pemberton.

'Of course! You had such a dreadful cold the last time I saw you,' Irene continued to smile, causing Bevin to realise how her father—never having seen the other side of Irene—could have been taken in by the woman. 'Aren't you going to invite me in?' she asked, and while Bevin was thinking over her dead body would she invite this woman into Jarvis's home, Irene was pressing on, 'I've never met your fiancé, but I'm sure...'

'Ah!' Warning bells began to go off in Bevin's head as, rooted to the spot, she determined not to let this woman over Jarvis's threshold. But even as she began to see how this falsely smiling woman might have appeared as a charmingly smiling woman to her father, she *had* seen the other side of her, and knew which was the true side.

'You really have landed on your feet, dear,' Irene simpered.

'How did you know where I was?' Bevin cut her short, and saw that Irene did not care one bit for her tone.

'It wasn't difficult!' she replied a shade tartly. 'There wasn't a picture of you in the paper or anything like that, but when I read that Mr Jarvis

Devilliers—the same Mr Jarvis Devilliers of that engineering group—was shortly to marry a Miss Bevin Pemberton, it didn't need a genius to put two and two together. You're a sly one,' she went on, her smile back in evidence. 'I didn't even know you knew him! But since there aren't too many Bevin Pembertons in this area, and since the paper gave this Court as his address . . .'

'What have you come for?' Bevin interrupted her smarmy flow.

'Why, to congratulate you, of course. Good gracious, Bevin, surely it's only natural that as your stepmother—soon to be stepmother-in-law to Mr Devilliers . . .' Irene inserted—but at the sudden greedy light that came to her eyes, Bevin all at once knew exactly why she was there.

'Money!' she cut her off before she could say another word. 'You've come here hoping for some money.'

'Must you be so vulgar?' Irene exclaimed as if the thought had never entered her head, her phoney smile swiftly vanishing.

'Vulgar or not,' Bevin replied, 'I haven't got any.'

'Don't give me that! Jarvis Devilliers is loaded!' snapped Irene, revealing much of her true colours. 'This flat alone must have cost a bomb! Why, you're living in the lap of luxury, while I . . .'

'Actually,' Bevin cut her off, the decision made without her having think about it, 'I'm coming home today.'

'You're coming back?' echoed Irene.

'That's what I said,' Bevin replied firmly.

'Well, naturally you'll want to be married from Abbot's Cheney,' Irene recovered her poise to begin to smile falsely again, clearly not ready yet to say goodbye to anything that was going.

But Bevin wanted this woman away from this place where, albeit briefly, she had known what it felt like to be happy. 'I'll see you there,' she told her, and wishing her goodbye, she closed the door. She knew then that just as Irene had spoiled her home in Abbot's Cheney, so she had just spoiled any idea Bevin might have had of staying in Jarvis's apartment until Sunday as he'd suggested.

How could she stay those extra couple of days now? Not when Irene knew where she was. The woman was capable of anything. If she could calmly turn up at her home in Abbot's Cheney and within twenty-four hours—and without a qualm—claim what was morally not hers, then, having scented money, there was no saying what the woman would not do for her own avaricious ends.

Bevin felt then that she would put nothing past Irene. Which meant, as she'd instinctively known without having to think about it, that she must leave Jarvis's apartment.

For a few sad moments she gave thought to leaving a meal ready for him to put in the microwave when he came in. Then she remembered that Mrs Underhill might appear at any time and, if last Friday was anything to go by, would have another casserole or something similar in mind to leave ready for that evening.

It did not take Bevin long to get her few belongings together, and in about five minutes flat she was ready to leave the apartment. She knew that when she wasn't there when Jarvis arrived home he would know she had returned to her home. But somehow, after all his kindnesses to her, it just didn't seem right to leave without writing a note.

Having decided on that course of action, though, Bevin went to his study and found pen and paper— and then had the utmost difficulty in knowing what to put. She wanted to thank Jarvis so much for the way he had housed her and looked after her. She wanted to explain all about Irene's visit, and how she had again spoiled things for her, and how because of the greed she'd seen in her stepmother's eyes, she just had to leave. But Bevin started to be afraid then that anything lengthy she might write might well reveal a little of how she felt in her heart about him. So, after much thought, she finally wrote, Dear Jarvis, My stepmother called here. Everything's getting too complicated. Thank you very much for looking after me. Bevin. That done, she slipped her note in an envelope and left it on his desk where he would see it—and quickly left the apartment.

Although the area was new to her, it nevertheless did not take her very long to find out in which direction to go. But as she walked into the town centre Bevin wished with every step of the way that she hadn't had to leave.

She tried to look on the bright side, but by the time she reached Dereham's bus terminus and was seated on a bus about to leave for Abbot's Cheney, she hadn't found too much that was bright. In fact, as the bus started off, all she could see was that, now she had left Jarvis's apartment, there was absolutely no necessity for her and Jarvis ever to see each other again!

It certainly wasn't necessary for them to see each other in order to keep up the pretence of their engagement, that much was for sure. For that matter, he had no need to ever so much as think of her again. Jarvis now had a cover which would keep his family from giving him a hard time for a while, so he would most likely feel free to date any one of the lovely women he would know.

Suddenly jealousy, which had up until that point been a stranger to her, began to nip. So that by the time the bus dropped her off at her stop, Bevin was convinced that Jarvis would no sooner find her gone from his home—probably before he read her note— than he'd be on the phone fixing up a dinner engagement for that evening.

She sighed when, with still some time to go before midday, she walked up the long garden path to her home, and mentally braced herself to deal with whatever mood Irene was in. But Irene wasn't in any of the downstairs rooms, and, as Bevin took in that what had once been a pleasant home had, in the week she had been away, been turned into an untidy grubby tip, she went upstairs to change.

She half expected that Irene, who had been up extraordinarily early for her that morning, might have come home and gone back to bed. But, as Bevin went by the master bedroom, shuddering at the clutter in there, she observed that, bed unmade, Irene wasn't there either.

Fifteen minutes later Bevin was hard at work getting her home back to the way she liked it. She was still cleaning up when at just after three a taxi pulled up and Irene got out.

'I didn't expect you back so soon,' Irene commented as she came through the door, and as Bevin looked at her she could almost see her stepmother trying to decide whether it was in her best interest to be pleasant or hostile. 'I've had lunch out,' she volunteered, clearly deciding, for the moment at any rate, Bevin realised, on the former. 'Naturally you'll have discussed with your fiancé about your coming back to Abbot's Cheney today,' Irene at once got down to essentials.

'Naturally,' Bevin agreed.

'So we can probably expect him to call for you here,' she simpered.

'Probably,' lied Bevin, and took herself off out of Irene's way, and went to clean the upstairs bathroom—realising then that not only did Jarvis not know her address, but that he had no idea she lived in Abbot's Cheney.

While she cleaned and scoured the bathroom, Bevin went over every conversation she'd had with Jarvis, but try as she might, she could not remember ever telling him that she lived in the village of Abbot's Cheney. Suddenly then she realised that, since her father had always insisted on them being ex-directory, there was no way in which Jarvis could look up her surname, and more important, her address, in the book.

A moment later, though, her heart lifted when it came to her that since Jarvis had made contact with the market research firm she had worked for by getting their name from her work-folder, he could as easily have seen her address on several pieces of paper in that same folder.

Not that he would be making contact with her, she realised, as severe and stolid common sense all too soon stormed in and she realised just how totally ridiculous she was being in imagining that he would. Why would he want to phone her, for goodness' sake? He now had the cover of being engaged, and any minor problem that might arise from then on he could, she full well knew, handle with both hands tied behind his back.

She was going to have to accept, she realised, that he was never going to contact her. Nothing—certainly not the fact that she wanted to hear his voice again, wanted him to phone her—was going to alter that.

Having established that unarguable fact Bevin nevertheless nearly jumped out of her skin when, having returned to the sitting-room an hour or so later, she was passing by the phone when it rang.

'That'll be your fiancé, I expect,' boomed Irene from her armchair at the other side of the room; and as idiotic as she knew it was, Bevin could do nothing about the way her heart leapt.

As calmly as she could she picked up the phone and said hello—and promptly, while she berated herself for being so foolish as to let herself get carried away by Irene's comments, her heartbeats settled down to a dull beat.

'I believe congratulations are in order!' Oliver Taylor stated stiffly.

'Oh—hello, Oliver,' Bevin answered, feeling constrained to answer him all of a sudden. 'Er—I thought you were visiting your mother until Saturday,' she remembered suddenly.

'I came back early,' he explained, and, not to be put off, 'What's this about your engagement?'

'Oh—you've—um—read about it?'

'I didn't need to! Thanks to Mrs Pemberton, it's all over the village!'

Oh dear, Bevin thought, this was something she hadn't considered. Thank you, Irene! But Oliver was waiting for her to give some sort of answer—and she didn't have one. 'You've been—to your shop?' she queried stiltedly, realising as she said it that he must have done, but some part of her brain still thinking he was having the complete week off work.

'Is that all you can say?' he asked, and Bevin felt more uncomfortable than ever—Oliver was sounding hurt, and even though she had never had any sort of a romantic understanding with him, he had been a good friend when her father had been ill.

'I'm—sorry, Oliver,' she apologised. 'It isn't...' she halted, barely knowing how to go on, then found he had put his own interpretation on her stilted manner.

'Mrs Pemberton's listening, isn't she?'

Avidly, and to every word, Bevin could have told him. But, 'Yes,' she replied.

'Well, we must talk. I think you'll agree you owe me that,' he said.

From the friendship he'd shown both her and her father, she supposed she did. So, 'Yes,' she said again.

A few seconds passed then with neither of them saying anything, then, 'We could talk freely if you were somewhere else,' said Oliver, and asked, 'Can you come and have a meal with me?'

'When?' she asked.

'Tonight, if you're free. I could pick you up just after six and we could go away from the village and into Dereham,' he suggested.

She was free every night, not just tonight, Bevin thought glumly, but at the thought—not so Jarvis, he'd probably be out with some luscious female this very evening—jealousy was all the prod she needed.

'I'll see you just after six, then,' she told Oliver, and came off the phone, to be soundly rounded on by Irene.

'You're never keeping up that friendship with Oliver Taylor!' she began.

'I'm going out for a meal with him, as a matter of fact.' Bevin thought she might as well tell Irene now as when Oliver called for her.

'You never are! You want your head examined!' Irene screeched. 'How can you think of playing around with someone who'll never be more than tuppence above a beggar, when you're engaged to a man who can give you everything?'

Irene's harangue followed Bevin up the stairs as she went straight away to get out of the clothes she had been working in and to take a shower. Had she been in love with Oliver then Bevin knew it wouldn't have mattered to her what his finances were, or were likely to be. But she wasn't in love with him, she was... She turned up the pressure of the water as though trying to drown out thoughts of the man who haunted her head and her heart.

There was a renewed onslaught to her eardrums when she passed by the sitting-room on her way out. 'Don't think I'm going to cover for you when your fiancé comes knocking at *my* door,' Irene let fly venomously, and Bevin was glad to get out.

She knew then that, short of asking Oliver for a dose of poison with which to lace Irene's tea, she was going to have to do something about finding other accommodation. But as she reached the end of the garden path, and Oliver leaned over from the driver's seat to open the passenger door for her, she had, for

the moment, other priorities than finding another
home.

'How are you?' Oliver asked as he started up the
car.

'Fine, thanks, and you?'

'Quite well,' he replied, and Bevin was stuck to
know what to say next.

'How was your mother?' she remembered to ask.

'Quite well,' he answered, and, never having been
out with Oliver before, Bevin thought, slightly
ashamed of the feeling, that she could only be glad
she was not going to have to repeat the experience.

Oliver took her to a pleasant restaurant in Dereham,
where the food was good. But as pleasant as the restaurant was, and as good the food, Oliver wasn't
Jarvis, and she didn't want to be where she was, but
back with the man she loved.

'This is a super place!' She did her best anyway,
for it wasn't Oliver's fault that Jarvis could make a
conversation about sawdust seem exciting while Oliver
seemed to have the unhappiest knack of making the
most exciting matters sound dull.

She wondered if it would be different if she had
never known Jarvis. Perhaps Jarvis had made every
other man dull for her. Then she remembered how
when Oliver had proposed that time, she had known
straight away that she would never marry him—and
that had been before she had met Jarvis. But... Her
thoughts broke off—Oliver was looking tense again,
like that time he had asked her to marry him, and she
knew they had come to the point of why they were
having a meal away from her home, and Irene in
particular.

'Where did you meet him?' Oliver suddenly asked out of the blue.

'Is it important?' she asked.

'No,' he replied, 'not at all really. I'm far more interested in us, you and me, than him and you.'

'Oliver——' she began, but before she could formulate the tactful words to tell him there was never going to be any 'us' as far as she was concerned, he noticed her ringless left hand.

'You're not wearing an engagement ring!' he suddenly pounced.

'There—hasn't really been time...' she began to prevaricate, and felt dreadful about having to lie. Though, as she thought about it, since there was never going to be anything between her and Oliver, wasn't it better this way?

'But what about *us*?' Oliver was asking, clearly not interested in any side other than his own. 'I thought you were going to think about us—think about marrying me?'

Bevin had no recollection whatsoever of giving him that impression, and certainly no recollection at all of saying she would think about marrying him. But, unhappily, rather than hurt his feelings by telling him so, all she could do was to simply sit mute.

Though when he asked, 'Don't you feel *anything* for me?' Bevin knew that by remaining silent she was hurting him more.

'I do, of course I do,' she assured him, but as his look swiftly changed to one of hope she had no recourse but to fall back on the truth. 'But I love Jarvis Devilliers,' she told him, and felt she admired Oliver more than at any time when he took that on the chin.

'You're saying you'll never marry me?'

'I'm sorry, Oliver,' she said unhappily.

There seemed little to be said after that, and the drive back to Abbot's Cheney was as silent as the drive to Dereham had been. Though this time when Oliver pulled up outside her house, he got out of the car and came and stood by her garden gate with her.

It was a dark night, but in the glow of a street lamp she could make out that he was feeling very depressed. 'Goodbye, Bevin,' he bade her quietly, and she knew then, from that goodbye—and not goodnight—that unless she went into his pharmacy to see him, she would never see him again.

'Goodbye, Oliver,' she said sadly, and stood quiet when, for the first and last time ever, he put his arms around her and kissed her.

He walked swiftly to his car and she turned to open her garden gate. Oliver had started up his car and was away before she was through it and her spirits were low as she thought of how good he had been to her father, and how it upset her to have to repay him by turning him down. But then suddenly all thoughts of Oliver went shooting out of her head when, though she had not heard a sound, someone came and grabbed her by the arm and swung her round.

A cry of alarm sprang to her lips—but never left her. For her alarm swiftly turned to joy, wonderful joy when, in the glow from that same street lamp, she recognised the man who had caught hold of her. He was tall, fair-headed, and was a man she had so jealously thought would be dining with some gorgeous girl that night.

But, even as that joy flooded through her to actually see Jarvis again, she quickly masked how she was feeling. For she was swiftly recognising too, from the fierce thrust of his chin, that Jarvis was not likewise affected with joy. Indeed, he was absolutely furious about something, she could tell, when, with his fingers gripping angrily on her arm threatening to cut off her circulation, 'I'll say it's all too *complicated*,' he quoted her note back at her on a snarl, and demanded toughly, 'Who the hell was *that*?'

CHAPTER SEVEN

To HER disbelieving ears, it sounded to Bevin just as though Jarvis felt he had every right to know who Oliver was. But, when in her view that was carrying any pretence engagement much too far, just to see Jarvis again had weakened her. She knew then that she'd have to find some backbone, or go under.

'How did you know where I lived?' she fired with all the spirit she could muster.

'You think it a mystery when you left your office folder in my car?' he rapped, but was far more interested in having his other question answered, it seemed, for, giving her arm a none-too-gentle shake, 'Who was he?' he challenged forcefully.

'Not that it's got anything to do with you,' she retorted, 'but Oliver's a friend—and you're *hurting my arm!*'

Abruptly Jarvis pushed her arm away, though he was no less aggressive as he snarled, 'For all his passionate kisses, he can't be *that* much of a friend!'

Passionate! Oliver? 'Just what are you getting at?' Bevin tilted her chin an angry fraction to demand, feeling as angry with Jarvis as with herself that, though she didn't want to argue with him, she seemed powerless to stop him needling her into doing just that.

'What would I be getting at,' he paused, and then added succinctly, 'little virgin?' And while Bevin was sorting out that Jarvis could only mean that she wasn't so involved with Oliver, or so swayed by his lovemaking either as to have gone completely overboard, he was going on to demand, 'Have you told him about our engagement?'

'We're not engaged!' she erupted, having had previous experience of the Devilliers gift for pushing her into a corner, and not liking it any better, even if Jarvis was the one doing it.

'Your stepmother believes we are!' he rapped—and suddenly the stuffing went out of her.

'You've spoken to Irene?' she asked him quietly.

'I called earlier,' Jarvis replied, and suddenly the aggressiveness seemed to have left him too. 'She invited me in—but I had other business to attend to,' he revealed.

'Oh, Jarvis!' she exclaimed softly, as it suddenly came to her what he was doing at her home. 'You came to see if I was all right?'

'After my excellent nursing, I should let you go without a follow-up visit?' he questioned, his voice sounding faintly amused in the darkness. But a touch of gruffness had entered his tones when he questioned, 'You *are* all right here, Bevin?'

No, she wanted to tell him. No, I'm not. I want to be with you. But, 'Yes, of course,' she stood there and smiled. Then, because she just yearned to lay her head against his chest and beg him to take her with him—and feared she might—she took a step backwards. And wished she hadn't when she straightaway realised that Jarvis had seen that movement away from him as an indication that she wanted to go in.

'Goodnight, then,' he bade her, and while Bevin was suddenly feeling too choked to dare to say a word, he took her by the shoulders, dropped a light kiss on

her temple, and, as she raised a hand to the place he
had kissed, he turned and walked away.

She went swiftly up her garden path with emotions
so out of control, it was all she could do not to burst
into tears. Fortunately Irene had the television set on
and turned up loud, so that Bevin was able to slip
straight upstairs to her room.

Oh, Jarvis, Jarvis, Jarvis! she cried inwardly, and
had the quickest wash on record, the sooner to get
into bed and pull the bedclothes over her head. She
was never going to see him again.

With thoughts of Jarvis in her head, she did not
sleep well. There was something final in his visit that
told her that this was the end of it. She'd known that
before, of course, so to see him again tonight had
been a bonus. But oh, how good of him to come and
check that she was all right!

Lying awake for hours in the darkness, Bevin wondered if the business he had been on was somewhere
in the direction of Abbot's Cheney. Perhaps that was
why he had called a second time. He must have been
passing and decided to call when he'd spotted her
getting out of Oliver's car.

His anger at seeing her in Oliver's arms was quite
understandable too, she realised. She hadn't said anything to Jarvis about there being any man in her life—
because there wasn't any man, in that sense, in her
life. But with Jarvis wanting the cover of being engaged, he wouldn't want her confessing the phoniness
of that engagement to anyone she was on kissing terms
with. He wasn't to know, of course, that that was the
one and only time Oliver had kissed her. Though—a
small smile of love curved her mouth—it hadn't taken
Jarvis long to decide—and let her know about it—

that her embraces with Oliver had not been all-
consuming.

Bevin was still inwardly restless when the time came
for her to get up, and she was glad to leave her bed.
She had a shower and got dressed, then went downstairs and made herself a pot of tea, and stood
drinking it while she stared out at the February
weather. She took heart from the fact that, for a
change, it looked as though it was going to be a nice
day.

The weather seemed about the only nice part of the
day, though, for when Irene got up at around eleven
she was in a particularly unpleasant mood.

'Your fiancé called here last night looking for you,'
she announced.

It was on the tip of Bevin's tongue to tell her that
she knew, that she'd seen Jarvis, but that greedy light
was there in Irene's eyes again, and Bevin decided at
that moment that she did not want to discuss Jarvis
with the woman.

So, since good manners decreed that she answer
with something, she murmured politely, 'Oh?'

'Oh, indeed!' snapped Irene. 'The least you could
do is thank me for lying for you!'

'You lied for me!' Bevin exclaimed, but then
realised that if Irene had lied for her, it was only because she hoped there was something in it for herself.

'I told him you'd gone into Dereham to see an old
friend.'

'Thank you,' Bevin said quietly—then discovered
that Irene thought she deserved more thanks than that.

'I could always tell him, *any time*,' she stressed,
'that the *old* friend you were with wasn't so *old*. And
that you didn't merely go to see him, but that he called

here for you—and that, in fact, it was a prearranged date!' she ended nastily.

Bevin did not miss the threat, the blackmail threat, behind Irene's words, and it sickened her. 'You could,' she agreed quietly, and feeling in need of some fresh air, she went and did some work in the garden.

Saturday and Sunday passed interminably slowly, but when on Sunday Bevin again found that she couldn't stay in the same house as Irene, she took herself off for a long walk.

By Monday she was feeling so down that for a while she thought she'd been hit with post-flu depression. But it wasn't just that, though that could have been a contributory factor. Nor was it just the fact that Irene, and the situation which had been caused by Irene claiming her home, was getting her down. The root cause, Bevin very well knew, was the fact that she was in love with Jarvis and was aching for a sight of him, yet knew full well that she had as much chance of seeing him as she had of Irene leaving.

On Tuesday Bevin tried to pull herself together. What she needed was a job, she decided, and she scanned the paper, but saw nothing for which she was qualified. She got out her writing case to apply for two jobs anyway, then found that Irene had come into the room and was eyeing the writing case in her hand.

'If you want any help drafting out a marriage agreement—and wedding day settlement, of course— I can . . .'

'Marriage agreement . . .?' Bevin cut in, horrified.

'You've got to look after your own interests!' Irene asserted. 'I'm only thinking of you!' Since when? Bevin could scarcely believe what she was hearing.

But as Irene smiled falsely, Bevin knew she would not
be living in the same house as Irene for much longer.

She took her notepaper up to her room and wrote
out her job applications there. She did not go down
again until she heard Irene go out. Then she returned
to the sitting-room, took out the Yellow Pages di-
rectory, and found quite a few estate agents listed. A
short while later she began telephoning around to find
out what possibility there was of renting some
accommodation.

She came off the telephone realising that her funds
were going to be stretched to the limit if she moved
out before she had found a job. Even then, given that
accommodation to rent was scarce, from the starting
price of rental quoted she was going to be very hard
pressed to make ends meet—even if she was lucky
enough to find somewhere.

She was just wondering if accommodation was any
more plentiful, or any cheaper, in Illington, and was
on the point of phoning a few estate agents in that
town, when suddenly the phone started to ring.

The phone seldom rang, so she answered 'Hello',
fully expecting it to be a wrong number—then she
clutched at the phone as if it was a life support system.

'How's my favourite patient?' she heard Jarvis ask.

In shock, was the answer to that, but, 'Thanks to
some terrific health care, I think I'll make it,' she
managed to return lightly.

'You're eating properly?' he enquired, just as
though he knew that she was not.

'Of course,' she answered after a moment of
hesitation.

'Which means of course—not,' he saw straight
through her reply. 'I don't know, little Bevin,' he

teased, and she loved his good humour, 'what I'm going to do with you.' Take me back to live with you, she wanted to tell him, but naturally said nothing of the kind. Then she found that no answer was necessary anyway, because suddenly Jarvis had made a decision about what to do with her, and with her listless eating. 'Fancy having dinner with me?' he asked suddenly.

She knew she should say no. But, 'Er—n—when?' she asked, hoping she didn't sound too eager but as if she had a whole string of dates, but might be able to squeeze him in.

'Let's see,' he muttered, and she had an idea he must be consulting his diary, that he hadn't phoned her with the intention of asking her to eat with him, so was having to check for a free time. 'How about tomorrow?' he enquired, and, at the thought that in just over twenty-four hours she would see him again, all pretence left her.

'I'll look forward to it,' she told him honestly.

'I'll call for you seven-thirtyish,' he said, and rang off.

Bevin was in a state of euphoria for fully half an hour after Jarvis had rung off. Any feelings of depression she had been experiencing evaporated into thin air. She was seeing Jarvis tomorrow, she was seeing Jarvis tomorrow—what else mattered?

What did matter, she realised, as she began to come a little way back down to earth, was that she had nothing to wear. She consulted her watch. It was too late for her to go into Dereham now, the shops would be closed by the time she got there. But tomorrow—she refused to think about the dent she would make in her nest-egg—she would catch a bus and be in Dereham for nine.

'My goodness, you're all togged up!' exclaimed Irene, when at seven-fifteen the following evening Bevin, her newly washed hair shining, came down the stairs to wait for Jarvis. 'Is that new?' she wanted to know.

'Yes,' Bevin answered, and cared not at all whether or not Irene liked her purchase of that morning, because she did. The coffee-coloured button-through jersey dress, that ended just above the knee, had a matching three-quarter-length straight jacket, and never had she owned anything so elegant. She felt good in it and, without conceit, knew that it suited her.

'Who's it tonight—your fiancé, or the chemist?' Irene wanted to know.

'Jarvis,' Bevin replied, and knew that in her nervous pleasure to be seeing him again, she had come downstairs too early. 'Excuse me, I've forgotten something,' she murmured, and went back up to her room, to comb her hair again, and to convince herself that she looked as good as she thought she did.

She saw Jarvis's car pull up from her viewpoint at the landing window, and was downstairs when he came up the path and rang the doorbell. But any notion she might have had of bidding Irene goodbye and of going straight to the front door was lost when Irene, as if to establish that it was 'her house', and moving like greased lightning for such a big woman, got to the door first.

'Mr Devilliers!' she was crooning as Bevin came into view.

'Good evening, Mrs Pemberton,' he greeted her courteously, but smiling over her shoulder at Bevin. 'Hello, darling,' he said softly, and although Bevin knew the endearment was only there because her step-mother was there, her knees suddenly went to jelly.

'Hello,' she answered quietly as she squeezed round Irene, and felt her insides match the jelly of her legs when, taking possessive hold of her arm, Jarvis bent and placed a kiss on her cheek.

'Have a good time!' Irene, injecting syrup into her booming voice, suddenly brought Bevin back to re-alise that there was someone else in the world other than the man she loved.

'Thank you,' she murmured, and as Jarvis bade Irene a courteous adieu, she walked down the path with him thinking that this just had to be the happiest evening of her entire life.

Jarvis closed the gate and then went to open the passenger door of his car for her, and Bevin, mainly because she was starved for a sight of him, flicked a glance up at him. But at the serious look in his grey-blue eyes as he glanced down at her, her heart started to drum erratically.

Then his mouth suddenly quirked in a trace of a smile. 'You know, of course, that you're beautiful,' he commented.

It was what she needed to hear. Not that she was beautiful, but that Jarvis thought her so. 'Thank you,' she murmured, and slid elegantly into his car, with Jarvis waiting until she had her long silken legs neatly tucked in, when he closed the door.

Although she had not really known him long, the way they fell into an easy rapport, talking of every-thing and anything, seemed just like old times. Jarvis drove a different route to Dereham from the one the bus took, and entered the town from the northern end, then drew up at the town's most exclusive hotel.

Bevin felt as if she was floating on air when he escorted her inside and took her to an ante-room, where they sat beside each other on a low plush couch, and chatted away until a set of menus was brought to them.

Her experience of going out to dine was limited, but she in no way felt gauche or ill at ease, and had no idea what was responsible for that. It could have been Jarvis's relaxed manner rubbing off on to her, or that she felt good in her new clothes, or perhaps neither, but merely the fact that this evening was so unexpected, so wonderful, that she just had to grasp all that it offered with both hands.

She had a vague recollection of ordering something with salmon in it for a starter, and something with chicken and herbs for a main course. But as someone came and took her jacket off somewhere, and she sat in her elegant short-sleeved dress opposite Jarvis at a candlelit table, she had no recollection of what she ate. For he held her attention the whole time, either introducing some light-hearted subject that brought a smile to her face and occasionally made her laugh quietly out loud, or he would ask her opinion on some more serious matter.

Sometimes, too, it seemed that she was able to reach his sense of humour also, for several times he smiled at something she said. And once he leaned back in his chair after some comment she'd made, and seemed highly amused—though what it was she had amused him with Bevin could not for the life of her later remember.

Though Jarvis was neither smiling nor amused when, as she finished off with an ice cream and he cut into a piece of Stilton, he all at once pinned her with his all seeing grey-blue gaze, and enquired quietly, 'Seen anything of Oliver since Friday?'

Instinctively she went to answer no, ready to tell Jarvis that she doubted, unless she caught a glimpse of him passing, that she would see Oliver again. But suddenly she hesitated. She and Jarvis were getting on so well, but he was not a man who missed much. She'd about die if he guessed at her feelings for him— so wasn't it better to let him think that there was some other man on her horizon?

'He's been away for a few days,' she said truthfully. And because she wasn't at all happy with the deception she had just engineered, 'How about you?' she asked quickly.

'Me?' Jarvis questioned, plainly not getting her drift for once.

'Isn't there an—Olivia—in your life?' she enquired.

'What—and me an engaged man?' he lobbed back at her, and, even though he had neatly evaded the question, she just had to laugh again.

A moment later, though, she realised, 'That means that you haven't told your family the truth yet.'

Jarvis shook his head, then grinned the most devastating grin, as he told her, 'And life's bliss!'

What could she do? She laughed. His family had been giving him hell ever since they'd known the terms of his grandfather's will. He had earned a respite, and she was glad that she'd been of some help.

She was not so glad, however, when about ten minutes later Jarvis settled the bill, and an attentive waiter brought her her jacket. For it was a signal that this most wonderful evening was almost over, and she didn't want it over—not yet.

Which was why, as they were driving towards the northern outskirts of Dereham, she was absolutely delighted when, as they drove near the quiet avenue where he lived, Jarvis unexpectedly suggested, 'My place for coffee?'

'It would be better than mine,' she accepted, and was delighted again when, clearly on her wavelength once more, he seemed to know that there was no way she would invite him in if her stepmother was there. Come to think of it, in those circumstances he would have refused anyway, she realised.

It crowned her evening to be inside his apartment again. She'd been so happy with him here, she recalled, but then, as she went with Jarvis into the kitchen, she realised she mustn't look back. She couldn't have that time back again, so she must treasure what she had now.

'You'll be glad to see Friday, I expect,' she murmured impishly, surveying the general disorder that needed the hand of Mrs Underhill around, as Jarvis set about making some coffee.

'If you're referring to the fact that there's a general Wednesday look about the place, then I can only plead that I didn't know when I left here tonight that I'd be bringing you back for coffee,' he replied, his eyes on the merriment brimming in her large brown ones.

And she liked that. Liked the fact that, spontaneously, he had invited her back. That had to mean that he was enjoying her company as much as she was enjoying his, didn't it? Suddenly, though, his eyes had moved from her eyes and were on the curve of her mouth.

Her breath caught when she saw his amusement fade, saw that he seemed to still for a moment and, as laughter faded in her too, he suddenly raised his glance to her serious eyes. 'Come here!' he said gruffly, and the next Bevin knew, she was where she wanted to be—in his arms.

Willingly she stayed there, willingly, as his arms tightened about her, she gave him her lips. And when he kissed her she clung on to him—and clung to him again when he pressed her to him and buried his face in her hair.

With his arms around her, he moved with her from the kitchen and into his sitting-room, only taking his arms from around her when, with his mouth over hers, he unbuttoned her jacket and removed it.

His jacket was gone too when they moved to the couch and as one, his arms about her once more, lowered themselves into its hugging confines.

Lying with Jarvis on the couch, Bevin had no memory of kicking off her shoes. She only knew she was without them—as he was without his—when their legs and feet entwined. He traced kisses down her throat, and all shyness seemed a thing of the past when he undid the top buttons of her dress and pressed his lips to the swelling mound of her breast.

Nor did shyness return when, those few undone buttons not being sufficient, Jarvis undid the rest of her buttons and her dress fell open to reveal her satiny curving form.

'Beautiful, Bevin!' he breathed, and as a fire burnt fiercely and almost beyond bearing in her, he took her dress off and traced kisses over her shoulders while he moulded her to him.

'Oh, Jarvis!' she moaned in wanting, and had her mouth claimed again in burning kisses as he undid her bra and removed it.

When his warm caressing hands captured the throbbing swollen globes of her breasts she clutched on to him in an agony of wanting. Never had she known such a yearning, and as he removed his shirt she gloried in the joy of letting her hands, her fingers rove him.

'Sweet Bevin,' he breathed, and she was in torment for him when he lowered his head and captured first one pink hardened peak of her breast between his lips, and then the other.

'Jarvis!' she cried his name, and knew she would deny him nothing.

'You'll stay with me?' he asked, his mouth against her throat, his hands at her breasts moulding, caressing, and making a nonsense of her thinking.

'You're saying I can have my old room back?' she asked in delight. She wanted nothing better.

'I didn't mean—*that* room,' he murmured, and suddenly great clamouring warning bells were going off in her head.

Barely knowing where she was, but acting on some instinct to heed those warning bells or be lost, Bevin moved until there was some space between their two bodies. Then she didn't know whether she was grateful to Jarvis or not when, as though sensing all was not well with her, he moved her until they were both sitting on the settee.

'Problem?' he asked, holding her still, his warm hair-roughened chest burning against the side of her, one arm across her naked shoulders, as she strove with all she had to pull herself together.

Jarvis wasn't asking her to stay with him, to live with him, but to stay *for just one night*! Bevin wasn't sure about anything very much just then, but at the thought that all it would be was one night in his bed, she knew that all that mattered then was that Jarvis did not love her and, with an instant decision suddenly there before her, she knew she wanted more than that.

Somehow—and with his warm inviting body so close, she didn't know how she managed it—but somehow she made herself pull away from him. She knew when he immediately took his arm away from her that he would not force her; knew from that action that he had probably already read that, again having led him on, once more she was saying no.

'I...' she opened her mouth to apologise, but guessed it had gone beyond an apology. Yet she didn't want the evening to end with them on bad terms—even if, having led him on, she was to blame. So she swallowed, and did her best to find some of the earlier lightness that had been a constituent factor in making the evening go so well. 'Do you really think it would be wise to—er—consummate our engagement?' she asked huskily.

She wanted him to laugh, to say something light, anything so she should know herself forgiven. But he didn't laugh, and didn't say anything light, but seemed to take a juddery kind of breath as though seeking self-control. 'I'm in a state of not knowing where the hell I am!' he told her. Then, as if taking a severe grip on himself, he added, 'Perhaps you're right,' and the next she knew, he was pushing her clothes at her and growling, 'Come on, get dressed, I'll take you home.'

Bevin got dressed, Jarvis took her home, and she awoke in her own bed on Thursday morning—and half wished it were otherwise. There was that treacherous side of her that insisted, Wouldn't it have been better to have had one night of love with Jarvis than nothing? Against that, however, was the reality that equally insisted, But it wouldn't have been a night of love, would it? Of lovemaking, certainly. Of mind-blowing lovemaking, certainly—but what then?

Bevin spent a wretched Thursday, and then a wretched Friday, and an absolutely awful weekend with her thoughts going backwards and forwards over everything that had taken place—and with some part of her still wishing she had stayed the night with Jarvis, and had known the comfort of his arms.

By Monday morning, though, having chased her thoughts around in circles, she knew she should stop looking back. She had made her decision and, thinking positively, it had been the right one. And, since she was plagued by something she could no longer do anything about, for more positive thinking, she had better plan her future. As yet she had had no reply to her job applications, but that shouldn't stop her applying for other jobs. She'd try for jobs in Illington too. Though since she didn't want to have found somewhere to live in Dereham, only to find— she should be so lucky!—that she'd got a job in Illington, she'd better hang fire on the accommodation side of it until she had her job situation sorted out.

'For an engaged woman, you don't see very much of your fiancé,' Irene took a spiteful stab at her on Tuesday.

There were a dozen or so excuses ready on the tip of Bevin's tongue, but again she decided she didn't want to discuss Jarvis with Irene. 'That's true,' she said, and left it at that. But when she went to bed that night, it was to do some more positive thinking.

She must look to the future. A future that did not include Jarvis. Which meant that she would not go out with him again—not that he'd been hammering on her door pleading with her to go out with him again. It was almost a week now since he had driven her home, walked up to her front door with her, said, 'Bye, Bevin,' kissed her lightly on the cheek, and gone back down the path.

But should he, out of kindness, again ring and ask her if she was eating properly, then she must, without hesitation this time, assure him that she was. Pride, if nothing else, decreed that Jarvis should not feel obliged to see that she had nourishment. He had been goodness itself when she'd been ill, calling in a doctor and everything. But let that be an end to it. She was no longer living under his roof—she didn't want him to feel he had to be responsible for her.

Wednesday passed without the telephone ringing once, and Bevin went to bed early that night to relive the fact that a week ago tonight she had shared a meal with Jarvis, and it had been quite wonderful.

By Thursday she knew he was never going to contact her again, and that all future days were going to be as grey as the one she was living through now.

By Friday she was ready to answer the most un-likely job advertised in the paper. Irene was being more of a pain than ever in that while Bevin was doing her best to put Jarvis out of her thoughts, Irene had taken to carping on and on about him.

'It wouldn't do for me, I can tell you,' she boomed, apparently ticking the days off on her calendar since Bevin had last seen Jarvis. 'You two haven't had a row, have you? You want to watch it! Men like him don't come your way all that often! As it is, it wouldn't surprise me if...'

Bevin had discovered that the best way to deal with Irene's diatribe was to close her ears to it. She did so then and, having absolutely nothing in common with the woman—apart from the same surname—she was heartily glad when Irene went out for the afternoon.

Bevin was upstairs checking through the things she would take with her when she moved, when all at once the phone rang. Leaving what she was doing, she flew down the stairs to the sitting-room—then halted. It wouldn't be Jarvis! And if it was, she wasn't going to go out with him. But it wouldn't be him. Though, just in case it was, and he rang off... Suddenly she was galvanised into action and rushed over to pick it up and get a 'Hello' out before the caller could assume no one was in.

'How's Bevin?' Jarvis asked.

Oh, Jarvis, I love you so, she thought. 'Never better!' she answered brightly.

'Good,' he commented, and began to get to the purpose of his call. 'I wondered if you'd...'

'I don't think,' she cut him off, as she grabbed urgently at a stray strand of strength before it could escape, 'that it's a good idea for us to go out together again.' There, she'd said it—and felt not one whit better for the effort.

There was a chilly silence emanating from the other end of the phone, but although Bevin knew that, having said her piece, she should now quietly say goodbye and put the phone down on its receiver, she just could not.

Then Jarvis was speaking again, his tone changed to silky, mocking. 'Put your panic away, little virgin,' he instructed. 'The invitation isn't coming from me, but my parents.'

'Your parents?' she exclaimed, in agitation, not panic.

'I haven't wanted to worry you,' Jarvis explained, mockery gone, 'but they've been putting on the pressure this week. They insist on meeting you, and I,' he paused, then quietly let fall, 'finally agreed that we'd go down to the Manor tomorrow.'

'We?' she choked hoarsely.

'You and I,' he cleared up any doubt.

'But I *can't*!' she protested, and heard his voice short, sharp and with no nonsense about it.

'Why not?' he demanded. 'If you've some prior arrangement, then...'

'I haven't,' she cut in. 'But...'

'But nothing,' Jarvis refused to listen to any excuses. 'I'll call for you tomorrow afternoon.' He paused, but only briefly, and when she did not argue, 'Bring a bag—we'll stay overnight,' he told her, and rang off, and Bevin was left staring at the phone in her hand.

She put it back on its cradle, then went slowly back up the stairs, still stunned at her quiet acquiescence. So much for all her 'I won't see him again' lectures, she thought. But, as a smile started somewhere deep inside her, she knew that, loving him the way she did, there was nothing else she could do but go with him.

CHAPTER EIGHT

BY NOON on Saturday, Bevin, who had made another lightning visit to the dress shops in Dereham, was in a tense state of wondering just what she thought she was doing. How could she go with Jarvis and deceive his parents into thinking she was going to marry him?

By one o'clock she was wondering—how could she not? Jarvis needed her. Half an hour after that and she knew that the fact of Jarvis needing her still did not make it right. At two o'clock she was thinking along the lines of how she'd allowed Jarvis to use her in this 'engagement' so far without putting up any protest, so what was she quibbling about now? Indeed, if there had been any irritation from anyone at this 'engagement', that irritation—not to say fury—had, initially, come from Jarvis.

In an attempt to get the subject which had been whirling around and around in her head off her mind, Bevin pulled her thoughts nearer home. Irene, for one, had been much cheered to know that she was going with Jarvis to spend the night at his parents' home. Not that Bevin had made up her mind what, if anything, to tell Irene of her plans. But when Irene had returned home yesterday, and had said spitefully, around seven, 'And I don't suppose you'll be seeing your fiancé tonight either!' she had been stung into telling her,

'By the way, Jarvis and I will be spending Saturday night at his parents' home.'

Irene had been sickeningly sweet after that. Though Bevin had kept out of her way as much as possible. Which was why she was now standing, dressed in her best trousers, shirt, sweater and jacket, with her overnight case by her feet, looking out of the landing window. She was on the point of again wishing she'd asked Jarvis what time he would call, when all at once his car pulled up outside.

Many emotions darted through Bevin then as, not waiting for him to come up the garden path and ring the doorbell, she picked up her overnight case and went swiftly downstairs. Irene must have been watching from a downstairs window, Bevin realised, as she met her in the hall.

Irene had her hand on the door catch and had pulled back the door when Bevin said courteously, 'Goodbye, Irene,' and was halfway down the path, with Jarvis already coming up the path to meet her, when Irene's voice boomed after her.

'What time will you be home tomorrow, dear?'

Dear! Bevin turned. 'I'm not sure. Goodbye,' she said, and turned, to have Jarvis take her case out of her hand.

'Bevin!' he greeted her with an inclination of his head, but did not this time salute her cheek with his lips.

'Hello, Jarvis,' she answered quietly, and was in his car with him, her case stowed, pulling away from the kerb, when she sensed that he was as tense as she was.

Perhaps he didn't like deceiving his parents either— even if they had, along with his sister Rosalind, made life pretty unbearable for him of late. 'How have you been?' he enquired, but to her taut emotions the question had seemed an effort.

'Great,' she replied. 'You?'

'Terrific,' he grunted, and that was about the sum total of their conversation for the next half-hour.

Then, 'Where are we going, by the way? I've no idea where your parents live?' she felt she should know.

'Didn't I say? Bedfordshire.'

That lasted them for another half-hour. Then, when Bevin was about to ask another question, some perversity in her nature mingled with tension and pure straightforward nerves, and the words wouldn't come.

Not so, though, when Jarvis steered his car up a long drive and pulled round to a large and elegant brick-built manor house, stopped the car and got out. Panic was rife in her as he came round and opened the passenger door and helped her out.

'How am I supposed to act?' she asked swiftly.

'As though you were my fiancée,' he answered levelly. But suddenly the tension she felt in him seemed to be fracturing, and a moment later there was a hint of amusement playing around his mouth as he added, 'As though you feel the sun rises and sets with me.'

'Heaven help us!' Bevin tossed at him sarcastically. But, unexpectedly, the tension in her was dissolving too, and as the amusement on his mouth deepened, all at once they were both laughing—and at that moment his parents came up to them.

'We heard your car!' Helen Devilliers, a tall, stately woman in her late fifties, smiled pleasantly, kissing her son in greeting, and turning to Bevin, did not wait for him to perform the introductions. 'Bevin!' she smiled. 'We've so looked forward to this day.'

'How do you do,' Bevin said formally, but was kissed on the cheek too, by both Helen Devilliers and her husband.

Lawrence Devilliers was about five years older than his wife and was tall like his son. Though any pangs Bevin experienced at the warm welcome she received from Helen Devilliers were edged out by his father's sharp attitude. 'I'm glad someone can bring a smile to Jarvis's face; he's been like a bear with a sore head lately,' he told her.

Whose fault is that? she wanted to defend Jarvis, but had an idea that the number of people who stood up to Lawrence Devilliers could be counted on one hand. Then she discovered that she was not actually the sort of person who would always smile pleasantly for the sake of peace, and say nothing, though her expression was pleasant just the same when she replied, 'Either you've got the knack, or you haven't,' and glancing at Jarvis as the four of them headed into the house, she was sure she had espied a warm look there for her.

It cheered her and came to her aid in the next half-hour as they sat in the graceful drawing-room and took tea. And when later she was shown up to her room and was alone, she thought of that warm look she had glimpsed, a tingle of admiration there too— dared she believe, and it helped her whenever she thought of the ordeal dinner that night could turn out to be. For it had transpired, over the teacups, that Rosalind and her husband Milo were expected to join them for dinner that night.

For all Bevin knew, Rosalind and her husband might dine at the Manor every Saturday night, but somehow she didn't think so. Somehow she had a feeling that Jarvis's sister was to be there to add to the pressure on him to marry before July. Pressure, Bevin realised, which she, since she was supposed to be engaged to him, might well come in for too!

Bevin spent quite some time worrying about what might happen over dinner. But by the time she was dressed in her new purchase of that morning, a calf-length dress of fine wool, its amber shade going particularly well with her hair, she had come to terms with the situation. Good heavens, she thought bracingly then, Jarvis had had months of pressure to put up with. If she couldn't stick it out for a few hours she'd be too pathetic for words! In any event, Jarvis would be there too, and if things did get a bit heavy, she knew she could rely on him to come to her aid.

For all her bracing thoughts, though, she privately owned to being nervous when Jarvis came and knocked on her door to take her down to dinner.

'Ready?' he asked, looking immaculate in his white shirt and dinner jacket.

'I'll just get my bag,' she replied, and turned back into her room, nerves giving way to a wildly beating heart at the admiration that had *definitely* been in his eyes.

She went down the wide and handsome staircase with him feeling never more glad that she had hared into the shops in Dereham that morning. She was more glad than ever when in the drawing-room Rosalind, wearing a dress that must have cost the earth, looked over at her.

'Bevin!' she exclaimed, and coming over to her, 'How nice to see you!' she beamed, and, half turning to a stocky man a few years her senior, 'Come and meet Milo, my husband.'

Milo Williams was sandy-haired, and quiet, and very much in love with his wife. Which, Bevin later observed when with Helen and Lawrence Devilliers they were seated around the dining-room table, was fully returned by Rosalind.

Jarvis had once told her that, as well as having a cold and calculating streak, Rosalind had some very lovable traits, Bevin remembered. But as dinner got under way, and Rosalind began to slant all her questions around the 'engaged' couple, Bevin was hard put to it to find anything very lovable about Jarvis's sister.

But she managed to smile on, and even had a brief discussion on the subject of gardening with Helen Devilliers before, the main course served, Rosalind plainly felt too much time was being wasted in pleasantries, and abruptly asked Jarvis point-blank, 'Just when *are* you going to get married?'

For the briefest of seconds, as all eyes turned to Jarvis, Bevin thought she saw ice glint in his expression as he looked at his sister. Then, though Bevin knew that he would have no problem in fielding the question, he suddenly looked away from his sister and to her, paused for a moment, then smiled. She smiled encouragingly back—then got the shock of her life when he said, 'I'm afraid, Rosalind, that Bevin is insisting on keeping me waiting.'

How, as all eyes swung towards her, she kept her jaw from falling open, Bevin couldn't have said. But, as she recalled how she had thought she could rely on him to come to her aid—yet here he was dropping a very awkward ball in her court—she began to get angry. He knew full well, as she knew full well, that there was never any question of them getting married—much less that she was keeping him waiting.

'How thoughtless of us!' Helen Devilliers was gently inserting before Bevin could erupt. 'No wonder you want to wait—you've only recently lost your father, Jarvis tells us.'

'Yes, that's true,' Bevin said quietly, suddenly realising that since his parents must have asked Jarvis something about her, about her background, it was only natural he should mention her recent bereavement.

But even as she accepted that, she saw Lawrence Devilliers send his wife an exasperated look, so she wasn't totally surprised when he abruptly took the conversation back where he wanted it, by asking abruptly, 'Jarvis had told you the terms of his grandfather's will, I take it?'.

She refused to look at Jarvis. 'Yes,' she replied briefly.

'Then could you not consider marrying before his birthday?' he asked, still in the same abrupt tone, and Bevin did look at Jarvis then. But while his look was steady on hers, he was not doing a thing to come and help her out, and she began to feel angry with him again.

For two pins, she thought, she'd tell everybody she'd marry Jarvis tomorrow if he wanted. However, only the fact that that was much too close to the truth saw her biting down on such a statement—which left her only one reply available. 'I need to—think about it,' she told his father.

'Well, while you're thinking about it,' he said, 'you might take into account the fact that this house, the estate, are a constant drain on my resources.'

'Yes, all right,' she murmured—but the pressure didn't end there.

'Jarvis's mother and I would know much more peace from financial stress in our declining years,' he went on, 'if the fortune due to me was guaranteed.'

Declining years! Heavens, Bevin thought, this just a sample of what Jarvis had had to put up with—his parents weren't past their sixties yet, by no manner of means old or declining these days! But, having realised that Lawrence Devilliers was laying on the 'hearts and flowers' bit with a trowel, Bevin might out of good manners have not argued the matter. But just then, at the very moment she saw Rosalind, who had seemed about to put in her twopennyworth, give a glance at her father, she caught the barely perceptible way in which Lawrence Devilliers shook his head at his daughter. And Bevin discovered then, as she accurately read that action as Lawrence Devilliers telling Rosalind to leave it to him, that he thought he was getting through, that, good manners or no, she just couldn't stay quiet.

So she smiled sweetly as she looked directly at Lawrence Devilliers, and asked him innocently, 'Couldn't you sell the house and buy somewhere smaller?'

Oh, my word, she thought the moment the words were out—talk about stunned silence! She moved her gaze from the apoplectic-looking head of the household to his daughter and caught her frosty glare head-on. Bevin flicked her glance past her to where even Milo was looking decidedly unfriendly. Even Helen Devilliers, who seemed to have a far sweeter disposition than any of them, was looking out of sorts, she noted as her gaze moved on.

With what she had said having such an antagonistic response, Bevin hardly dared to look at Jarvis. But she steeled herself to do so, and when she did, she could have hit him! Because he, out of all of them, was the only one who looked as though he would burst out laughing at any moment. The swine! He thought it was funny!

'*Sell* the Manor?' Jarvis's father's getting his breath back to exclaim in horrified tones caused Bevin to transfer her attention back to him. 'This house has been in the Devilliers family for generations!' he informed her.

'Oh,' she murmured.

But she was nearly cringing with embarrassment when he went on, 'I need that money to keep it in good repair for you and my son. It will be yours and Jarvis's one day,' he underlined.

Oh grief, Bevin thought, and was silent and couldn't wait for the meal to end. When the meal was over, however, and they adjourned to the drawing-room, and whether they thought her rude or whether they didn't, she almost at once made noises about returning to her room.

'Do you require anything?' Helen Devilliers asked her with a sincere smile.

'No, thank you, Mrs Devilliers,' Bevin answered, and was on her feet and heading for the drawing-room when Jarvis came over to give her a 'fiancée's' special goodnight. But, love him though she might, Bevin, who had had enough of his family for a while, had had more than enough of him.

He had his back to the room when by the drawing-room door he caught hold of her arm. To his credit, though, she realised that he must have read from the fuming look in her eyes that he'd get short shrift from her if he attempted to kiss her goodnight. 'Any problems?' he murmured so that no one else might hear, circumspectly keeping his distance.

'Just the one!' she hissed, and didn't know how she got out of the room without boxing his ears, when his answer was to grin broadly as though he found her reply highly amusing.

Up in her room Bevin paced about knowing that *Jarvis Devilliers* was the biggest problem she was ever likely to come across. He knew full well why she was angry too—him and his 'I'm afraid Bevin is insisting on keeping me waiting'! He and his whole family wanted dropping in a compost heap from a great height! Well, she qualified, perhaps not his mother so much—but one way and another it had not been the most successful mealtime of her life!

All in all she was glad to get into bed and pull the covers up over her head. Never had she thought she might want to get back to Irene, but when Bevin thought how it wasn't done yet, and how in the morning the pressure would still be there, she wished she was back in Abbot's Cheney.

She slept badly, was awake early, and, hearing sounds of movement about, decided she'd had enough of bed. She showered and dressed in yesterday's trousers and a fresh shirt, then went downstairs to search out the possibility of a cup of coffee.

She found the breakfast-room without any trouble, but saw trouble in the fact that she was not the only one down. Jarvis was already at breakfast, as was his sister, and from appearances they'd already exchanged a few short, sharp words.

However, Jarvis seemed to put his irritation with his sister to one side when he saw Bevin. 'Good morning,' he greeted her pleasantly, and pulled out a chair for her at the table.

'Good morning,' she replied civilly, making that one good morning do for the two of them as Jarvis poured her a cup of coffee and set it down near her.

'What would you like to eat?' he enquired. 'Mrs Horton will be in presently and...'

'Nothing for the moment, thanks,' Bevin interrupted. She was not hungry and did not require the housekeeper to prepare anything for her.

A brief silence settled over the room, but she had barely taken a sip of her coffee when she received an endorsement that she hadn't been mistaken when last night she had thought that the pressure would still be on today for her and Jarvis to name the wedding date. For Rosalind, wasting no more time than that, was looking across at her and challenging, 'I simply can't understand why you're being so stuffy about not getting married straight away.'

Bevin sought round for a covering reply, because while she might not be feeling very friendly to Jarvis just now, she still loved the swine—and love and loyalty went hand in hand. She found then, though, that she did not need a covering reply, because whether Jarvis and Rosalind had been exchanging harsh words before she'd arrived on the scene, and this was just an extension of it, he was suddenly answering for her by telling his sister curtly, 'Leave it, Rosalind.'

'Why should I?' Rosalind wanted to know. And, to speed a flare of pink to Bevin's complexion, 'You've been sleeping together! Bevin practically lives at your place! So what's the differ...'

'Bevin does *not* live at my apartment!' Jarvis cut his sister off sharply.

'Much!' she scorned. 'From...'

'The only reason Bevin was there—and in my pyjamas,' he forestalled any interruption Rosalind might have attempted to get in with, 'was that she was quite ill with what the doctor who attended her diagnosed as flu and shock. As for Bevin's sleeping with me,' he defended her furiously, 'there are *some* women who actually say *"no"* to sleeping around!'

'Good heavens, you're saying that Bevin's pure and...'

'Believe it!' he rapped.

By this time Bevin was staring from one to the other in amazement. It was as though she didn't exist! 'My... Good...' Rosalind attempted, and seemed to be having the utmost difficulty in taking in what her brother was telling her. 'Well, I'll be...' she tried again. Then suddenly, as if recalling that Jarvis had said before that day that Bevin had been ill the Sunday she had called, and perhaps suddenly realising that Bevin had been more flushed from a high temperature than from anything else, she all at once turned to Bevin, and, showing a very different side from her normal one, said sincerely, 'I apologise, Bevin. It seems that my comments just now were very much out of order.'

By then, though, Bevin had already had quite sufficient of both Jarvis and his sister, and without a word or another look at either of them she promptly pushed her chair back from the table and exited the breakfast-room.

She almost went upstairs and back to her room, but what she needed was some fresh air. Without

thinking about it further she went marching to the
front door, and was soon striding out first around the
paths of the lawns, then down to the gardens beyond,
and finally out through a gate at the bottom and into
some fields.

Rosalind Williams, for all her sincere apology, was
a dreadful person, but Jarvis Devilliers was worse!
He'd as good as told Rosalind she was a virgin, Bevin
fumed, when it was no thanks to him that she was.
If he'd had his way and she had stayed that night in
his bed as he'd ...

Her thoughts abruptly shut off as suddenly she
became aware of footsteps striding after her, of footsteps nearing. But she had built up another head of
indignant steam when all at once, as he fell into step
with her, Jarvis dropped his jacket over her
shoulders—and just the feel of the jacket that had
known his body now warming hers was destroying.

Weakened though she was, however, she kept her
head, and kept marching on. She hadn't given thought
to the coldness of the day outside as, clad in a thin
shirt, she had stormed angrily out of the house.
Although the mood she was in then, as she again
started to grow angry, all she could see in Jarvis's
action in following her was that, with her other dose
of flu so recent, he didn't fancy being lumbered with
her should she get chilled to the marrow and bring
on a second helping of it.

Bevin's anger towards Jarvis was spurred on by the
fact that while she walked furiously, he seemed to only
easily stroll along beside her. Though it surprised her
that, while he must know that she wasn't too delighted with him just then, he hadn't simply left her
to get on with it, but was still there with her.

She began to slow her pace as they approached a five-barred gate, though by the time they reached that gate, Bevin knew she couldn't take any more. It had been a mistake for her ever to have come here. But, despite her high-flown notions of how she had been going to tell Jarvis she wouldn't go out with him again, she had, deep down, greedily wanted to have more time with him. But in that greed lay disaster. It was time to end it—now!

Abruptly she halted, looking up into his calm grey-blue eyes. 'I'm ready to go back to Abbot's Cheney whenever you are!' she announced snappily.

By the merest flickering of his eyes, she could tell that he wasn't too enamoured by her tone, yet he remained calm, casual even. 'I'll see to it,' he agreed, and, shrugging, 'Any particular reason?' he enquired.

Reason! He wanted reasons! 'Where would you like me to start?' she erupted, and not giving him a chance to tell her, 'How about, and I quote, "I'm afraid Bevin is insisting on keeping me waiting"!' she hurled at him.

But still he kept his cool, and she wasn't sure that a note of mockery hadn't entered his voice when he drawled casually, 'Would you have me so ungallant as to tell everybody listening that I was in no hurry to marry you?'

That hurt—even if she had known from the outset that besides his being in no hurry to marry her, marriage to her did not remotely figure in his plans. 'Well, I'm not happy at all about this deception we're playing on your family!' she flared hotly.

'You'd rather marry me to show that it isn't deception?' he enquired shortly, and her breath caught.

'At the risk of sounding repetitive,' she found the spirit to fire, 'get lost!'

She would have swung away from him then, but as she made to move, suddenly he shot out an angry hand to detain her. 'Or is it that you've someone else in mind to marry?' he demanded.

She stared up at him, her emotions suddenly in one gigantic jumble, and suddenly, too, she started to feel desperate. Desperate, and as though, since he clearly didn't care for her, he should know that somebody did. 'Yes!' she yelled. 'Since you must know, yes. *Yes, yes, yes!*'

'*Who*?' he thundered, and never had she seen him look so enraged.

'It's none of your business!'

'Oliver!' he made a furious but accurate stab. 'The man you were kissing the Friday you left me! He's asked you to marry him?' he demanded blazingly.

'And if he has?' she challenged, and suddenly her heart was pounding frantically against her ribs. Had she got it wrong? Did Jarvis care—a little bit?

Fate gave a hollow laugh at just how wrong she'd got it. For his answer was to fling her arm away from him, and to show just how much he cared, 'Then marry him, and be damned to you!' he snarled, and swinging round, he went striding back to the house.

Bevin could not have felt more beaten had Jarvis given her a physical blow. So much for her craziest flight of fancy yet. Far from growing enraged because he objected to the thought of her marrying Oliver, he'd sounded more as if it would please him to give her away at her wedding.

Bevin stayed where Jarvis had left her and used the next five minutes to pull herself together. Then she

spent another five minutes in realising why Jarvis had
been so enraged just now. Quite plainly he'd been extremely annoyed that, having so furiously defended
her virtue to his sister, he'd since learned that she was
engaged to some other man—and had been engaged
to some other man—the whole time she had been so
passionately clinging to him, ready and willing, eager
even, to engage in some heavy lovemaking.

At the end of those ten minutes Bevin stuck her
head in the air, and headed back to the house. That
lovemaking hadn't been all one-sided, she thought
angrily, nor was she going to be looked down on by
anyone—and certainly not by Jarvis Devilliers!

Rosalind was crossing the hall when she went in—
and she was another whom Bevin, with new as-
sertion, wasn't going to be looked down on by either.
'You're leaving straight away, so Jarvis says!' Rosalind
exclaimed, but she clearly thought there was more to
it than that—and wanted to hear more.

'Believe it!' Bevin replied curtly, and dropping
Jarvis's coat down on an antique chair in the hall,
she had started up the stairs when Rosalind's voice
reached her.

'Lord,' she tossed after her, 'you're getting just like
him!'

The drive back to Abbot's Cheney was not
brimming over with joy—nor was it conversational.
Bevin filled in the time the journey took in thinking
of how sweet Jarvis's mother had been when they had
said goodbye. 'Come again soon,' she had urged, 'and
stay longer this time.'

'Any chance of my being your matron of honour
in the spring?' Rosalind, not one to give up easily,
had questioned on the drive of the Manor house.

'Not a chance!' Bevin had told her, and when Rosalind's face cracked into a humorous smile, Bevin all at once realised she could quite like Jarvis's sister.

'Let's meet in town one day?' Rosalind suggested. Though before Bevin could think of a suitable answer, Milo was bidding her a pleasant farewell—as was Jarvis's father. In fact, everyone seemed to be at their most pleasant—except Jarvis.

Bevin thought she would be glad to reach Abbot's Cheney, but when Jarvis, insisting on carrying her case up the path, did no more than nod curtly in parting, she didn't know how she felt.

'Didn't you bring Mr Devilliers in?' Irene questioned crossly—and Bevin plummeted to new depths.

'There didn't seem much point,' she replied, and before Irene could argue the case, 'I doubt if I shall see him again,' she said flatly.

'You've *never* broken your engagement!'

'I-it was mutual,' Bevin replied, wanting nothing more than to go up to her room and shut the world out—but there was to be no such luck.

'You stupid bitch!' Irene shrieked. 'How could you turn down the chance of a lifetime like that! You want your head examined, letting an excellent catch like that wriggle off the hook!'

Jarvis wriggle—*never*! 'It's a private matter.' Bevin, who felt too wrung out to want to stay and argue, found she was doing just that.

'Not when it concerns me, it isn't!' cried Irene, her voice rising.

'Concerns you? How?' Bevin asked, against her better judgement—and was quite nauseated to hear Irene, flying off at a tangent, let out a stream of invective which boiled down to the fact that the only reason she had allowed her to stay on so long was that she was sure Mr Devilliers would wish to recompense her.

That was when Bevin left her and without another word went straight to the small storeroom where the large cases were kept. Taking two cases with her, she went straight to her room and immediately set about filling them. Then she found that even her own room wasn't sacrosanct when, without knocking, Irene suddenly came in and took in what she was doing.

'You're leaving?'

'I should have done that the day you moved in,' Bevin retorted.

Bevin awoke on Friday to a dull March day, in her dull bedsit, and contemplated the day before her without enthusiasm. Life was dull, dull, dull—and she wanted Jarvis.

By no means for the first time, though, in the almost five weeks since she had bidden an abrupt goodbye to Abbot's Cheney, Bevin gave herself a severe talking-to on the subject and the fact that Jarvis was unattainable, and that she had better buck her ideas up.

She got up and, looking for pluses as she forced herself to do most mornings, she again tried to cheer herself with the thought that she was luckier than most of the occupants in her particular block in bedsit land. She did, minute though they were, have her own private bathroom facilities and, if good fortune was on her side, she might soon be moving into somewhere much larger.

She was under the shower when she allowed her thoughts to play back over the recent weeks. She had been so emotionally churned up when she had packed

her cases and struggled with them to the crossroads
that she'd barely known what she was doing, she recalled. In fact, she'd felt so defeated that it hadn't
mattered a jot then where she went. The first bus to
come along had been one bound for Illington. She
had got on it with some vague notion of getting off
the bus near Illington railway station, and taking a
train to London.

She had been at the station when, out of all that
was so much of a quagmire in her head, she was suddenly certain of one thing in particular, and that was
that she did not want to catch any train to London.
Jarvis lived in Dereham and, while Illington wasn't
Dereham, she wanted to stay close to the same area.

She had spent that Sunday night at the nearby
railway hotel and, knowing she must find somewhere
cheaper, had gone out and been lucky the next
morning to be in the right spot at the right time when
a bedsit with its own facilities became vacant. It wasn't
what she was used to, but nothing was what she was
used to any more.

Barely waiting to deposit her luggage, she had then
gone looking for work. Her luck lasted when a week
later she was offered the position of receptionist-cum-
clerical assistant for an insurance company.

It didn't take her long to settle into her new job.
She got on well with the people she came into contact
with, and found the clerical work well within her
capabilities. She had been in her job a week, however,
and was seeing Jarvis in every tall, fair-haired man
who walked by the office, when she read in the paper
that the Devilliers Group had just taken over
Openshaw Engineering. Since that Sunday when,
without a word, Jarvis had dropped her back at her

old home, she had so many times been over every
conversation, look and nuance shared with him. This
time, though, as she again heard his voice as this time
he asked, 'How do you feel about us being "engaged" for as long as it takes for me to get something
achieved in this take-over?' she knew that this really
was the end. For she had agreed to be 'engaged' to
him until then—until the take-over was fact. And it
now was fact and, although she had walked out on
her 'engagement' three weeks ago, she had still felt
tied to Jarvis.

Bevin abruptly ceased looking back when the
shower water—as was its caprice—suddenly started to
run cold. Snatching at a towel, she got busy drying
herself, and, when thoughts of Jarvis refused to go,
she again gave herself a lecture on the theme of
bucking her ideas up. Jarvis accompanied her all the
way to her place of work.

'Is it tonight that you're going to look at that flat
in Arlingford Road?' Tracy, one of the women she
had grown friendly with, enquired as she came by to
drop some paperwork on her desk.

'Yes,' Bevin answered. 'Any time after seven, the
advertiser said when I rang.'

'Well, best of luck,' Tracy bade her, and went back
to her own office.

Bevin got on with her work, reflecting on how she
had checked her finances, and had come to the conclusion that she could just about afford something a
little more spacious than her present abode. Then
Jarvis was back in her thoughts again, and as her pen
flew over the work before her, she mourned that she
would never see him again. He had no way of finding

her address this time—fate gave a hollow laugh because, come to that, no way would he want to.

That Friday stretched as every day stretched, but
Bevin eventually left her office at a little after five.
Since, though, there seemed little point in catching a
bus back to her bedsit, only to snatch a cup of tea
and catch another bus back again, she decided to stay
in the town centre and have a look around the late-
opening stores.

Turning a corner, she entered Illington's High
Street. Then, when she truly thought she was coping,
and would swear she hadn't thought of Jarvis for at
least ten minutes, there in front of her was a travel
agent's window. It was a branch of the same travel
agent which he had halted by that Friday a lifetime
away.

She halted too, and was transfixed as for ageless
moments she stared and stared unseeing at the travel
agent's window. Oh, Jarvis! she thought unhappily,
and could have wept. How kind he had been to her
that night—that night when she'd gone up to him and
said 'Excuse me...'

'I wonder if you'd mind...'

That voice wasn't hers! Utterly astounded, certain
that she had Jarvis so much in her head that she was
now hearing his voice not only in her mind, but in
her ears too—though she'd never heard him say that
before—Bevin nevertheless just had to swing round
to make sure he was not there.

Swiftly she turned—and all but collapsed when, as
if he was afraid she might dart away, a firm hand
came and caught a firm hold of her upper arm. Her
breath caught, then she wasn't conscious of breathing

at all, for she was looking up into the grey-blue eyes of a tall fair-haired man.

She opened her mouth, but no sound would come, so that all that she could do was look up into his stern face and stare hypnotised at the pulse that jerked in his temple. How long she stood mute she could not have said, but she was still in a state of shock when Jarvis grated, 'I was going to ask if you'd mind coming with me,' and, as that pulse throbbed away, 'But on second thoughts, I *insist* that you come with me.'

Bevin had by no means recovered when, with a firm grip on her arm, Jarvis steered her, too stunned to protest, across the road to where his car was parked.

CHAPTER NINE

BEVIN was in the passenger seat of Jarvis's car before her brain patterns had adjusted. She was awake, and it was actually happening—*now*! Then agitation took over.

Desperately she battled for calm, and managed to find an outward modicum of it as some polite part of her trotted out, 'It's very nice to see you again, Jarvis,' and, with nerves biting, 'But I've some business to attend to.'

'So have I!' he stated in no uncertain fashion, and while Bevin was shakily thinking in terms of reaching for the door handle and getting out of the car, Jarvis was going on to give her a choice—but no argument. 'Your place or mine?' he questioned toughly.

'What . . .?'

'We can't talk here,' he answered decisively.

Talk! 'We have nothing to talk about!' she declared categorically—but added urgently as he started up his car, 'I'm not going with you to Dereham!'

'So where do *you* live?' he countered, and steered the car into the milling High Street traffic.

'Huh!' she grunted, pride decreeing that he didn't see her poky bedsit with its shabby furnishings—pride decreeing that he shouldn't see that she didn't appear to have fared so well since the last time he had seen her.

That 'Huh!', though, was the last of the conversation for the whole of the journey to Dereham. Jarvis drove confidently and well, but seemed to have a lot on his mind. Although Bevin was agitated, she was still a mixture of happiness to see him again after such a long while, and apprehension at what he might think they had to talk about. His take-over of Openshaw Engineering was completed now, so he couldn't want her help in the 'pretend engagement' department any more. And if he wanted to tell her, formally, that the 'pretend engagement' was at an end, then she already knew that, so he needn't bother.

Her thoughts were still chasing rapidly one after the other when Jarvis pulled up at the Court where he lived. It occurred to her briefly to say he could say anything he wanted to her where they were, but as he got out of the car and came round to open the passenger door, she discarded the idea. From the look of him, he wasn't in any mood to put up with anything he might term as nonsense and, weak though she knew she was being, having come this far, she wanted to see inside his apartment again—that place where she'd been happy.

So silently she got out of the car, and silently she went into the building with Jarvis, and then up in the lift with him. 'You're looking thinner!' he commented as, putting his key in the door lock, he glanced down at her.

'You're not looking so fat yourself!' she retorted, and suddenly, in the way it so often happened, a spark of amusement lit Jarvis's eyes, while at the exact same time her sense of humour ignited and all at once she wanted to laugh.

She had a few seconds to get herself under control, however, when Jarvis stood back to allow her to precede him into his flat—and another few seconds in which to realise as she glanced up at him that she was mistaken about his amusement. For his expression was stern, with not so much as a glimmer of amusement in his eyes, as he indicated she should go into the sitting-room.

'Mrs Underhill's been today,' she commented involuntarily as she breathed in the faint smell of polish and noted how everywhere looked spick and span.

'Shall I take your jacket?' Jarvis enquired.

'No, thanks,' she replied, hoping that conveyed that she wouldn't be staying long.

'Drink?' he asked, and Bevin began to get the oddest notion that he was nervous about something. It wasn't like him to pussyfoot around. The Jarvis she knew would be more likely to wait only until he'd got the outer door closed before he started ripping into her with what was on his mind.

'No, thanks,' she replied again, but was already scorning—Jarvis, nervous?—don't be ridiculous! Of the two of them she was the nervous one, because she hadn't a clue about what, soon, he would be ripping into her about. 'Congratulations on the Openshaw Engineering take-over, by the way.' Her nerves were making her talk off the top of her head—why did she think he would be ripping into her, for goodness' sake? She'd done nothing wrong!

'You read about it?'

'It was in all the papers,' she explained, and as he looked levelly at her she felt nervous again, and in that nervousness, all at once she was babbling into speech to let him know, in case he didn't, 'So now, with the Openshaw Engineering business out of the way, there's no need for us to pretend to be engaged any more.'

His answer was to give her another direct look. Then, 'Take a seat,' he suggested, and came a step nearer. Bevin took a step back—and sat down on his huge, lovely and comfortable couch. Suddenly, though, she wasn't quite sure how she was feeling any more. When, however, he looked down at her from his lofty height and stated coolly, 'I'm not quite with you, Bevin. Why is there no need for us to be engaged any more?' her chief feeling was one of incredulity.

'Why, because the only reason we entered into it in the first place was the pressure you were under from your family, and your need to have your mind free to concentrate on other matters!' she exclaimed.

'Is that what I said?' he enquired, and all at once her thinking powers went foggy.

'I can't remember word for word,' she said, when only that morning she'd had no such problem, 'but that was the gist of it,' and was astounded by his reply.

For, suddenly taking it in his head to take a seat too, Jarvis came and sat down at the opposite end of the couch, and, turning to look at her, he commented evenly, 'It seems, little Bevin, that we've both gone in for deceiving each other.'

Oh, heavens! As if that 'little Bevin' wasn't weakening enough, she fretted, as she counselled herself not to panic. What had he found out? What did he know? 'You've deceived me?' she asked; the only way out of the corner in which he had again pushed her was to play on *his* deception. He couldn't know that she loved him, and was trying to hide it—could he?

'I'm afraid so,' he said, and from the suddenly strained look of him Bevin had the most peculiar notion that Jarvis was regretting having sat down and now, as though in need of some physical action, would prefer to be on his feet. But he remained where he was, and continued, 'Given that I've a soft spot for my family and would do a great deal for them— though I haven't the slightest intention of marrying just to please them,' he inserted, 'I'll admit there are times when one's family can be exceedingly annoying. But I enjoy pressure. In fact,' he owned, 'I seem to have the happy knack of thriving on it.'

'W... Y...' Startled, Bevin stared at him. 'But you said...' she managed to get a little further.

'I said I didn't need outside distractions,' he completed for her, seeming not to have forgotten a thing despite his earlier question of 'Is that what I said?' 'But,' he went on, slowly this time, for all the world as though he was carefully picking his way, 'I got them just the same.'

'In the shape of Rosalind barging into your meeting that day,' Bevin remembered—then looked at him, mystified, when, very deliberately, he shook his head.

'I got them in the shape of you, Bevin Pemberton,' he jolted her by answering, and, as her heart started to pound against her ribs, 'You've given me many problems one way and another ever since that Friday, eight weeks ago tonight,' he stated as if he'd counted every day and night of them, 'when you approached me in Dereham High Street and I found myself looking down into the most incredibly beautiful pair of eyes I'd ever seen.'

'Oh?' she mumbled, but it was more of a squeak than a question. She'd never known he thought her eyes incredibly beautiful. 'You were kind to me,' she found a stronger note to comment.

'Kind!' he repeated, though there was a hint of a smile at the corners of his mouth as he recalled, 'I'd worked late all that week and decided to give my PA a break by finishing early that Friday. I'd planned to do some work from home, but was passing through Dereham when I stopped to pick up an evening paper.'

'You didn't buy one,' Bevin chipped in. While she owned that some of that evening was still cloudy in her head, she clearly remembered that Jarvis had only just parked his car when she'd gone up to him. 'Well, not unless you stopped somewhere else first,' she qualified.

But Jarvis was shaking his head. 'Dereham was my first stop,' he confirmed, going on, 'and as you rightly said, I didn't buy a paper. I was about to, when I spotted that I'd parked by a travel agents and wondered for a moment if it might not be an idea to disappear abroad for a while without telling my family where I was going...'

'They'd been on at you about the—this—marriage thing that week?' Bevin questioned, and realised that she was bang on his wavelength when he smiled.

'Let's say their campaign had hotted up, and had ceased to be amusing,' he said. 'Anyhow, I was rejecting the idea of going abroad, knowing I'd got too much work on to take a break just then, when...' he broke off, and gave her such a warm look that her heart began to behave erratically once more '...when,' he resumed, 'there you were with your incredibly beautiful eyes. In fact, there you were, a beautiful woman.' Oh, goodness! Bevin thought, her lips parting as she caught a choky breath. 'Beautiful,' Jarvis went on, his glance going down to her parted lips and back up to her eyes again, 'but quite plainly ill.'

'I—er—wasn't feeling so good,' she attempted to throw in lightly, needing to say something to hide from this man with the all-seeing eyes the fact that she was a mass of emotion inside.

'You were *ill*,' Jarvis discounted her trying to make light of it, 'and in serious need of something to support you.'

'You opened your car and sat me inside,' she inserted quietly.

'And then discovered that you seemed to have an aversion to me taking you to your home.'

'I'm sorry,' she apologised. 'But it was good of you to bring me to yours.'

'I don't know about "good"—I was surprised myself! But it was obvious that I just couldn't abandon you on the pavement. Nor, with the state you were in, could I take you to a restaurant. You hadn't eaten that day,' he reminded her.

'Oh, dear. Was I a lot of trouble?' she asked apologetically. But suddenly she was struck by the stillness of him, by the silence that lengthened.

Then very quietly, but perfectly audibly, he said, 'I enjoyed having you with me,' and all at once Bevin was agitated again and even imagined there was an especially warm look there in his eyes for her.

But she must be mistaken, and she must keep her wits about her. 'Yes—well, it was very kind of you to let me stay,' she said hurriedly, then became a mass of inner disquiet at the steady way he was regarding her—just as if he had seen her nervousness, her disquiet, and was wondering at it.

Unbelievably, however, when she was sure, Jarvis being Jarvis, that he would want to know what she was nervous about, he did nothing of the sort, but instead recalled, 'You said something about me being kind *that* Friday night—and I think I answered something to the effect that I couldn't understand it.' He broke off, but his look was very direct. 'Nor could I understand it—until much later.' Though instead of explaining that to her, he continued, 'I came and checked on you many times as you coughed your way through that Friday night.'

'I remember seeing you once,' she agreed.

'And I remember wondering if I should take you to the Manor for my mother to look after,' he startled her by revealing.

'Your mother!' she echoed.

'You weren't going to get looked after if I'd returned you to that woman your father married, were you?'

'True,' she had to agree. 'But you decided against driving me down to the Manor.'

'The way my family were at me to marry, they'd have been certain—had I taken you swathed in warm blankets—that you must be extra special to me.'

'And you wanted to avoid the pressure of them ...' Bevin halted, feeling confused. Jarvis had said... 'But you thrive on pressure!' she exclaimed, and saw him nod as if he had been quietly waiting for her to work it out for herself.

'True,' he agreed. 'So the reason I gave myself for deciding against taking you to Bedfordshire was false,' he added, which was no help at all in clearing her confusion.

'False?' she queried.

'I'd told myself that I didn't want to take you there only to give them something to plague me with afterwards. But in fact, although I'd find their plaguing highly irritating, I'm quite able to cope with it.' Somehow, then, to be sitting so far away from her didn't seem to suit him any longer. For suddenly, making her heartbeat patterns peak frenetically, he moved and came and sat right next to her. And, looking deeply into her worried brown eyes, he confessed, 'Only later, my dear, did I face up to the fact that—I wanted to look after you myself.'

Bevin's breath caught in her throat, and she couldn't have moved then if she'd wanted to—and she didn't think she wanted to—though with his 'my dear' still ringing in her ears, she wasn't sure of anything any more. 'You wanted to look after me yourself?' she asked chokily, but just couldn't think straight, so she rushed on nervously, 'But you did take me down to Bedfordshire—I—later, I mean. You... We...'

'Exactly!' he commented. Though Bevin thought that if he believed that by taking hold of her hands he might have some calming effect on her, then he could not have been more wrong. Because she didn't know quite where she was when he took her hands in his, and, while her skin tingled from his touch, he resumed quietly, 'I wasn't looking after you then, was I? You'd gone from me back to Abbot's Cheney, and I...' Abruptly he broke off. And then, to her further agitation, '...and I,' he let fall, 'wanted to see you again.'

He'd wanted to see her again! What was he saying? Desperately Bevin swallowed on a knot in her throat. 'Your—parents—er—wanted to meet me,' she managed.

'I deceived you. I lied,' Jarvis owned.

'You lied?' she questioned, her lovely brown eyes wide.

'My parents weren't even expecting *me* that weekend,' he confessed. 'I rang them to say that *we* would be arriving, only when I'd got your consent.'

From what Bevin could remember of it, she hadn't so much consented as been *told*. But all at once there was more here than if she'd consented or been ordered. She could barely think straight—but she realised that for Jarvis to have lied had to mean that he was telling her something more than that he had wanted to see her again—didn't it? And if it did, what? She had no idea. But what she did know was that, quite unexpectedly, she was in no hurry to leave his apartment. Suddenly she wanted to stay. All at once she *had* to stay, and hear it all—whatever it was.

'Oh, Jarvis!' she cried helplessly, and just had to ask, 'Why? Why did you lie?'

For a few moments he did not answer her. But as she stared at him, he kept his eyes steadily on hers. Then, when she had no idea of what, if anything, he was reading in her eyes, and after drawing what seemed to her to be a breath of resolution, he murmured, 'Quite simply, I was missing you.'

Bevin couldn't have looked away from him then if she had wanted to, and, as her heart beat a riot within her, she just had to know more. 'Missing me?' she questioned chokily.

'Missing you—and finding that I couldn't bear the thought of spending the whole of the forthcoming weekend without seeing you,' he told her, and her heart beat faster yet.

'Oh, I see,' she murmured, but she didn't, not really, and she was just playing for time while she tried to keep herself from reading into what he was saying much more than he actually meant. 'So you decided, without asking your parents first, to ring and invite me to their home for the weekend,' she asked what seemed a fairly non-revealing question. Then she was thrown into confusion again when Jarvis shook his head.

'When I rang you that Friday five weeks ago, it was with the intention of asking you out to the theatre.'

'Theatre?' she questioned, puzzled. 'I don't remember your saying anything about the theatre.'

'That's because I didn't,' he explained. 'I didn't in fact get past the preliminaries before you were telling me you didn't think it a good idea for us to go out together again.' She remembered that, and the effort it had taken to say it. But there was that hint of a smile around Jarvis's superb mouth again, as he revealed, 'I couldn't have that, my dear.' And, while her look softened at that 'my dear', 'Equally, since I had to hide how vulnerable I suddenly felt, I had to invent something that would ensure I should see you, but at the same time wouldn't give away how I was feeling.'

'Oh,' she breathed huskily, and didn't then know which question she wanted to ask first. 'You were—er—vulnerable, you said?' she asked.

'It had never happened to me before,' he admitted, then added, succinctly, 'But then a lot of what's happened to me in the last eight weeks has never happened to me before.'

'Oh,' Bevin murmured again, but at the warm look in his eyes she found she was gripping hard on to his hands—or was it that he was gripping hard on hers?— she was so confused, she simply didn't know just which.

Though it was she who was very definitely gripping on, when Jarvis confessed softly, 'Learning to care, Bevin, has knocked me sideways.'

'Care?' she questioned huskily, the word, his word, burning in her brain, her heart.

'Oh, yes, care,' he breathed. 'Even while, with some stubbornness, I've been determined not to see it, I think I started to care for you from the moment I saw you.'

Her lips parted on a gasp of wonder, those two words 'for you' a symphony in her ears. But even as she tried to stay steady, her heart was singing. 'You did?' she gulped.

'I did,' he agreed, one of his hands leaving hers to brush a stray strand of strawberry-blonde hair back from her forehead. 'Though I'm not surprised if you didn't recognise it either, because I certainly didn't see what was staring me in the face for some time. But now,' he went on, his eyes studying, searching everything there was to be gleaned from her expression, 'now that I know, and think back, I'm no longer surprised that I brought you here that night you were in a state of collapse.'

'You're not?' she asked on a thread of sound.

He shook his head. 'Not now that what I couldn't understand has become clear. We were destined to meet, you and I.'

'Do you think so?' she asked with what voice she could find.

'I know so,' he answered, seemed to hesitate for a moment, then, 'You know what I'm saying?' he questioned.

Bevin swallowed hard, her nerves ragged as she grew desperately afraid she had got what he was saying totally wrong—because it just couldn't be true, could it? 'Tell me,' she said at last.

'You wouldn't say that if...' he broke off, and seemed to read what he needed to know in her expression, for, with his eyes fixed firmly on hers, he told her throatily, 'I love you, Bevin Pemberton.'

'Oh, Jarvis!' she sighed, and felt his grip tighten on hers.

'Is that it? Is that all?' he pressed urgently.

'You want me to tell you...'

'Most definitely.'

'I've been afraid you might see . . .'

'I didn't, so tell me before you finish the job and send me completely insane.'

'Oh, Jarvis, I do love you!' Bevin cried, and suddenly, blissfully, as a roar of joy left him, he had gathered her up in his arms.

He did not kiss her at once, but as if he had an overriding need to hold her, he just held her close up to him. 'Oh, my sweet one,' he breathed, 'I've so yearned to see you again, to be near to you again, yet sometimes I've despaired of ever finding you.'

'You've been looking for me?'

'Looking for you! I've haunted the shops in Dereham in case you'd found a job there and have been in daily contact with that market research firm you worked for in Illington in case you applied for some work with them.' Bevin stared at him open-mouthed. 'Then today, when I was feeling almost demented in my search for you, I had to go through Illington—something I rarely do—when I remembered I needed to get a card for my mother's birthday. I didn't—couldn't—believe my eyes when, having parked my car, I looked across the street and thought I saw you.'

'You didn't think it was me?' she questioned softly.

'I've seen you in so many women around the same height or with a hint of your hair colouring,' he confessed. 'Then you stopped in front of a travel agent's window, and you tilted your head in that way you have—and I knew—and in fear that you might vanish before I could get to you, I've never moved so fast in my life.'

'Oh!' she breathed, and knew then that he had known the same pain that she had known—and, warm in his embrace, she put her arms around him, and he kissed her.

How long they stayed like that, in each other's arms, sometimes exchanging kisses, sometimes just pulling back so that they could look into the face of the one they loved, and revel in the joy of knowing themselves loved, Bevin did not know.

But after some while Jarvis unhurriedly pulled back, and with his eyes on the jacket which she had earlier refused to part with, said softly, 'Unless you're in a desperate hurry to leave—and I warn you that until I know where to find you I'm not letting you out of my sight again—shall I take your jacket?'

She liked the sound of that 'I'm not letting you out of my sight' and wasted no time in shrugging out of her jacket—then found that Jarvis did not yet intend to let her out of his sight, for he did not leave the room with her jacket, but tossed it to the other end of the couch. Then he took her warm, shirt-clad body in his arms once again.

'That's more like it,' he declared. 'Now I can get really close to you and really begin to believe I'm not dreaming all this.'

'I feel much the same way,' Bevin confessed, and was pulled yet closer to Jarvis as he held her tightly next to his heart.

'Life,' he breathed against her hair, 'has been plain hell!'

'For me too!' she owned, and held on to him tightly too. Then tenderly he traced slow featherlight kisses over her face.

'Oh, this is so good!' he breathed. 'To have you here...' Words seemed to fail him, and in that emotional moment all her sensitivities went out to him.

'I love you,' she told him softly, and as his arms became iron bands around her, so many more minutes of silence ticked by as more barriers of disbelief came down, and confidence grew.

Jarvis kissed a corner of her mouth, then pulled back to look into her loving brown eyes, and Bevin, her bones melting, felt she was drowning. 'Oh, Bevin, girl,' he breathed, 'I love you with a love that consumes me.'

'Oh,' she sighed, but went on tenderly, 'Yet you said you've been determined—er—not to see how you felt about me?'

'Small good it did me!' he said wryly, and settled her comfortably in his arms. 'All the signs were there—almost from day one.'

'What signs?' she wanted to know, and loved him so much when he bent and kissed the tip of her nose first before, with that hint of a smile she loved curving his mouth, he obliged.

'Initially, signs such as bringing you here at all. Then being aware that I liked you, but venting my spleen on you just the same for not giving me prior warning that Rosalind had called the day before...'

'That was the Monday she phoned you at your office?'

'That was the Monday you, quite rightly, if politely, as good as told me to stuff my hospitality—and I discovered that I didn't want you to leave.'

'Really?'

'True—no more deceptions, I promise,' he smiled, and pausing to plant a light kiss on her mouth, went on, 'Then the very next night, not only did I find I was thinking about you on the drive home from the office, and actually enjoying the thought of having you there to come home to, but I just wasn't listening to warning bells when I felt not the slightest trace of alarm at how domesticated we seemed. I even went as far as to say I could marry you, and didn't heed any warning then either,' he owned. 'What I did feel, I remember, was quite staggered when—forgive me, my love, but I could think of one or two women who might have jumped at the offer—but not you. You turned me down flat.'

'You weren't serious anyway!' she murmured.

'Serious or not, suddenly everything was changing.'

'Changing?' she queried.

'Up until then you'd been a sweet young woman who'd been more ill than she'd realised,' he explained. 'But suddenly there you were, on the way to recovery and with flashing eyes to boot—and were quite something else again.'

A smile just beamed from her. 'Truly?' she asked.

'Truly,' he murmured, and kissed her tenderly. 'Oh, sweet love,' he breathed as he broke his kiss, 'I certainly should have taken heed when only the next morning I brought a cup of tea to your room, saw you beautiful in sleep—and felt my heart gentle for you.'

'Oh, Jarvis!' she sighed, and suddenly recalled, 'Oh, wasn't that the morning I woke up and reminded you about the groceries?'

'The same,' he agreed, 'and we both laughed, and I had to go quickly because all at once I was finding that I was enjoying that start to my day.'

'I'm glad,' she smiled.

'Wretched woman!' he said lovingly, and when she laughed, she was kissed very thoroughly for her payment. 'Where was I?' Jarvis asked throatily when, her response having been all he could have wished for, he drew back.

'Er—I think you'd just called me a wretched woman,' she surfaced, pink-cheeked, from her bemused state, to remember.

'So you are!' he growled. 'Have you any idea what you do to me, woman?'

'If it's anything like what you do to me, then—wow!' she exclaimed huskily, and loved it when he laughed.

'I'll second that,' he grinned. 'It was like that the first time we kissed, and you put up a sound reason for calling a halt, and I, my dear,' he murmured sincerely, his grin fading, 'started to fall most seriously in love with you.'

'Then!'

'Then,' he agreed, 'but I wasn't ready to accept why I should be thinking you so wonderful when, while I was still fighting with all I had not to take you back in my arms, you made me laugh again when you bluntly told me that my stated suggestion that we needn't pretend to be engaged was just me being passionate.' He smiled again. 'I should have recognised then, my wonderful woman, that I was in trouble,' he told her. 'Yet, even when I was unable to stop thinking about you and I spent the most restless night of my life, I stubbornly held out. Though while I was afraid, next morning, to bring you in a cup of tea in case when I saw you beautiful in sleep again, I should give in to an urge to kiss you awake, I wouldn't own then that there was more to what was going on inside me than just physical desire.' His look was deadly serious when he added, 'Little did I know that, when I'd deprived myself of seeing you that morning, I should come home and find you gone.'

'I couldn't stay,' Bevin told him. 'I'd realised, when I was in your arms the night before, that I was in love with you, and...'

'You've known since that Thursday!' Jarvis exclaimed.

'Do you think I'd behave like *that* with someone I didn't love?' she exclaimed teasingly in return.

'Do you know, I think I'm going to have my work cut out with you,' Jarvis opined—and Bevin burst out laughing.

'Anyhow,' she sobered to continue, 'I had to go. I knew Irene had only come here with money in mind. As I saw it then, I had to protect you from her avarice.'

'You—protect me? Oh, Bevin, Bevin, sweet love,' he crooned, 'do you think, when I've been able to cope quite adequately with the avarice of those I love for the past eight months, that I couldn't cope with the avarice of that woman for whom I care nothing?'

'Oh, Jarvis,' she mourned, 'I didn't want to go.'

'Honestly, love?'

'Honestly,' she replied. 'I was happy here.'

His expression showed his delight at that confession, and lovingly, in a tender moment of mutual need, they kissed. Then Jarvis was allowing some daylight between them, and was asking, 'So why, when I came chasing after you, were you...?'

'You came especially after me? I thought you had business that way!'

'So I lied,' he acknowledged. 'I couldn't believe you'd gone. Then I was damned if I was going to worry about you.' He smiled a wry smile as he confessed, 'Which is why an hour later I was refusing Irene Pemberton's invitation to come in and wait for her "dear stepdaughter" and went and parked up the road where I couldn't be seen while I waited for you to come home.'

'You waited for me?' she gasped.

'And for my sins learned the gut-twisting fury of jealousy!'

'Jealousy—you were jealous?' she asked incredulously.

'I've been pulverised by it!' he admitted, but returned to ask what had been his original question, 'So why, when you're in love with me, were you kissing Oliver Taylor?'

'I wasn't kissing him, he was kissing me,' she explained.

'But you allowed it.'

Bevin stared at him amazed. He really *was* jealous! 'It was the one and only time,' she told him, 'and it was a sort of goodbye—I'd told him that night that I was in love with you.'

'You *had*!' It was Jarvis's turn to be amazed.

She nodded, then confessed, 'Oh, Jarvis, you asked me if I was all right there, and I said yes, but I so wanted to go with you, it was breaking my heart!'

'Oh, love!' he cried, and held her against his heart for several healing minutes. Then he confided, 'If it makes you feel any better, sweetheart, I was missing you so much—for all you hadn't been in my home that long—that I just had to ring you a few days later!'

'That was the following Tuesday!' she remembered. 'You decided I needed feeding, and invited me out to dinner.'

'I'd intended to ask you out anyway,' he revealed, adding when she stared at him, startled, 'I've discovered, my darling, that there's more than a touch of perversity in this love business. There's nothing normal in it, anyhow. Because there was I, missing you and wanting to see you again, and urgently, so what did I do but, in order that you shouldn't know how urgently I wanted to see you, make arrangements to see you the next night.'

She'd had no idea that he'd missed her so, and could only stare at him in astonishment that when he'd phoned her that Tuesday it had been for the express purpose of asking her out. 'Oh, Jarvis,' she cried, and as she remembered, 'You called me "darling" that Wednesday too.'

'I should have recognised then that I was getting in out of my depth,' he grinned, and in answer to her mystified look, 'I promise you, sweet love, that I'm just not used to calling any woman darling. I was so pleased to see you, the word just slipped out.'

For seconds she just sat and stared wonderingly at him, then felt obliged to own, 'I was so happy to be with you that night.'

'It was the same with me,' he told her quietly. 'Is it any wonder that I found you so irresistible that I just had to have you in my arms?' he asked tenderly. 'Or any wonder,' he went on, 'that having driven you back to Abbot's Cheney, I should find it impossible to get you out of my head?'

'You tried?'

'I didn't stand a chance—and that was without my father or Rosalind mentioning your name daily.'

'But you stuck it out?' Bevin teased.

'For over a week I stuck it out,' he grinned. 'Then I rang intending to ask you to the theatre—and you know the rest. I called for you on Saturday to take you down to the Manor, not knowing where the hell I was. Then I discovered on Sunday just what *was* wrong with me.'

'You—realised—you loved me?' she asked, knowing now that he loved her, but still hardly believing that it was true, so wonderfully true.

'That was when,' he smiled, 'I'd just asked you if you had it in mind to marry someone else and, as you yelled "yes", jealousy started to tear me apart. And I knew, when you said Oliver Taylor had asked you to marry him, that I was in love with you, and that no one else was going to have you if I could do anything about it. Which, of course,' he added with a wry look, 'is why—love being the perverse creature it is—I told you to marry him and be damned to you.'

'Oh, darling,' Bevin whispered sensitively and, after a few quiet moments, 'That drive back was awful, wasn't it?' she remembered.

'Don't remind me! I've never been so stewed up in my life—in love with you, jealous with it, yet proud that there was no way you were going to know what you could do to me.'

'Oh, my dear love, was it as bad as that?' she asked softly.

'Believe it! I got no sleep that night, with my thoughts churning around and around. Surely it couldn't be true that you intended to marry someone else, I thought. Then, when I thought of all I knew of you, I began to feel that surely you wouldn't come away with me to my parents and stay overnight, if you were in love with some other man.'

'Oh, dear—you began to realise that I loved you?' Bevin suggested.

'It didn't come as easy as that,' Jarvis replied, taking hold of one of her hands and kissing it. 'Though I'll confess my heart did start to pound somewhat when, delving deeper, I started to wonder why, if you weren't in love with this damned Oliver, you should tell me that you intended to marry him. Could it be, I eventually got round to thinking, that you'd told me what you had because you needed a smoke-screen?'

'What did you decide?' she asked.

'I was in such a state by then that I couldn't come to any clear decision or conclusion. Though first I started to question now why you'd need a smoke-screen. You had no need... My thoughts seemed to halt right there as I recalled how because of my love for you I'd needed a smoke-screen and had found it in stating the opposite to what I was feeling in that "Marry him and be damned" outburst. Could it be, dare I ask, that, as I loved you, you loved me? By around dawn on Monday morning I knew only that I must see you. Then, remembering the way we parted, I started to have doubts that you'd see me. I thought I might phone you, but then I felt sure that you'd refuse to speak to me if I did. By lunchtime that day I was sure I'd soon be certifiable if I didn't get something sorted out, so I left the office early and drove straight to Abbot's Cheney.'

'Oh, darling—Irene told you I'd gone?'

'I couldn't believe it! No forwarding address, nothing! I started to go quietly demented when even Oliver Taylor didn't know where you might be.'

'You contacted Oliver?'

'Your stepmother told me where I might find him, and I went to see him. But the only joy I found there was that, since he didn't know where you were either, I felt I could take it as definite that you didn't intend marrying him.' A heartfelt sigh suddenly escaped him. 'So now, my dear, dear love, are you going to tell me where you've been and what you've been doing these weeks when I've been off my head trying to find you?'

Her first answer was to lean forward and to place her lips gently against his. Then, as he smiled, and his eyes showed he appreciated the voluntary and unsolicited kiss, she told him, 'What I've been doing is finding myself a job and working for an insurance company. Though first, since I couldn't afford to live in hotels, I went and found myself some accommodation to rent.'

'You've found a flat?'

'Nothing so grand!' she laughed. Nothing seemed to matter any more, not now that she knew that Jarvis loved her. 'I'm renting a rather poky, rather shabby bedsit,' she confessed cheerfully.

'Oh, my darling!' Jarvis groaned, and held her closely to him.

'But,' she went on some moments later, as she suddenly remembered, 'some time this evening I'm due to go and take a look at a flat that was advertised as . . .' Something in his expression caused her to halt. 'What . . .?' she began to question.

'My love,' Jarvis cut in, and there was no amusement in his expression, just total seriousness, 'if you really want to go and view some other accommodation, then without question I'll come with you to view it. But I would much prefer that when making plans to move from your present accommodation, you'd put my home at the top of your list of options.'

Bevin stilled, her mouth suddenly dry. 'What—are you saying?' she asked huskily.

'I'm saying, my own, that you, dear Bevin, *are* extra special to me, I'm saying that from the deep and abiding love I have for you, I want to spend the rest of my life looking after you.' Tenderly he placed a kiss on both her eyes, then drew back, to go on, 'I'm saying that the laughter, the sunshine, go out of my day when you're not here—that this place has been empty for me since you went.'

'Oh, Jarvis!' she cried, her voice barely audible, and he kissed her gently, reverently.

'I'm saying, my sweet love, that there's a readymade apartment waiting here for you when you're ready.' And suddenly, to make her heart race, he was cupping her face with his hands and telling her, his look adoring, 'I'm saying that, far from there being no need for us to be engaged any more, there's every need, and that I need, most urgently, to marry you.'

'You want to marry me?' she whispered.

'Oh, so much,' he breathed, 'and soon.' But then he qualified quietly, 'If you'll have me, sweet Bevin, I'll wait, and we'll have a July wedding—but no later than that.'

She looked at him, adored him, and all the love she felt for him blossomed up in her. Because quite clearly, while Jarvis was telling her that he wanted to marry her without delay, he was also telling her that he loved her so much that, knowing that he and his family would lose their inheritance, he was still prepared to wait until after his birthday to marry her.

'Oh, Jarvis,' she whispered, her heart gentle, her smile gentle. 'You don't have to wait that long.'

Next Month's Romances

Each month you can choose from a wide variety of romance with Mills & Boon. Below are the new titles to look out for next month, why not ask either Mills & Boon Reader Service or your Newsagent to reserve you a copy of the titles you want to buy — just tick the titles you would like and either post to Reader Service or take it to any Newsagent and ask them to order your books.

Please save me the following titles:	Please tick	√
RIDE THE STORM	Emma Darcy	
A DAUGHTER'S DILEMMA	Miranda Lee	
PRIVATE LIVES	Carole Mortimer	
THE WAYWARD WIFE	Sally Wentworth	
HAUNTING ALLIANCE	Catherine George	
RECKLESS CRUSADE	Patricia Wilson	
CRY WOLF	Amanda Carpenter	
LOVE IN TORMENT	Natalie Fox	
STRANGER PASSING BY	Lilian Peake	
PRINCE OF DARKNESS	Kate Proctor	
A BRIDE FOR THE TAKING	Sandra Marton	
JOY BRINGER	Lee Wilkinson	
A WOMAN'S LOVE	Grace Green	
DANGEROUS DOWRY	Catherine O'Connor	
WEB OF FATE	Helena Dawson	
A FAMILY AFFAIR	Charlotte Lamb	

If you would like to order these books in addition to your regular subscription from Mills & Boon Reader Service please send £1.70 per title to: Mills & Boon Reader Service, P.O. Box 236, Croydon, Surrey, CR9 3RU, quote your Subscriber No:...
(If applicable) and complete the name and address details below. Alternatively, these books are available from many local Newsagents including W.H.Smith, J.Menzies, Martins and other paperback stockists from 6th November 1992.

Name:..

Address:..

....Post Code:........................

To Retailer: If you would like to stock M&B books please contact your regular book/magazine wholesaler for details.

You may be mailed with offers from other reputable companies as a result of this application.
If you would rather not take advantage of these opportunities please tick box ☐